THE ORGANISED COOK

AMELIA FREER is one of the UK's most respected Nutritional Therapists and healthy eating experts. With a hugely engaged presence on both social and mainstream media, she has four best-selling books to her name and has helped thousands to adopt a happier, healthier life. She takes a scientific, holistic and compassionate approach to health and nutrition and is recognised for her calm, kind and considered approach. Amelia is a regular contributor to mainstream media and has extended her reach with regular appearances at public events, on podcasts and through her website, newsletter and social media channels. She also hosts sell-out workshops, cooking demonstrations and residential retreats. This is her fifth book.

AMELIA FREER

THE ORGANISED COOK

The Life-Changing Way to Save Time, Shop Smarter and Eat More Healthily

Lagom

First published in the UK by Lagom
An imprint of Bonnier Books UK
4th Floor, Victoria House,
Bloomsbury Square,
London, WC1B 4DA

Owned by Bonnier Books
Sveavägen 56, Stockholm, Sweden

Hardback – 9781788707077
Ebook – 9781788707084

A CIP catalogue of this book is available from the British Library.

Designed and typeset by Envy Design Ltd
Illustration by Envy Design Ltd
Printed and bound in Latvia.

Photography: Clare Winfield
Food Styling: Troy Willis
Prop and Set Styling: Emma La Haye
Hair: Philippe Tholimet
Make Up: Sjaniel Turrell
Editorial Director: Michelle Signore

1 3 5 7 9 10 8 6 4 2

Lagom is an imprint of Bonnier Books UK
www.bonnierbooks.co.uk

CONTENTS

For everyone who feels overwhelmed in the kitchen

INTRODUCTION

Have you ever started a new year, new week, or new day with the best of intentions to eat healthily, only for real life to get in the way and knock you off course? Do you find it impossible to resist the lure of the biscuit tin each time you make a cup of tea, or go to the supermarket for a few basics and end up with a trolley full of unplanned, not-so-healthy bargains? Are you concerned about the effect that nutritional inconsistency is having on your energy, health and vibrancy? And do you worry about the impact of your food shopping, both on your weekly budget and on the environment?

Would you prefer to feel calm, organised and on top of things in the kitchen?

If you answered 'yes' to any or all of these questions, then this is the book for you. If you're feeling a bit frazzled and frustrated when it comes to healthy cooking and eating you're absolutely not alone. Everyone struggles to eat healthily, consistently.

In this book you will find masses of practical tips, hacks, ideas and recipes to help you move from feeling overwhelmed to organised in your kitchen. These strategies will help to make your life easier and healthier – and hopefully a bit more fun, too! There's something so satisfying and soothing about a fridge filled with deliciously prepared food, ready to nourish our bodies whatever the week might throw at us.

Over the past 15 years as a Nutritional Therapist and writer, I have worked with thousands of people who have asked for my guidance on finding the 'best' diet. But I have come to realise that knowing what to eat for optimal health is just a small – albeit important – part of the puzzle. Up until now, this is where almost all the focus, writing and information on healthy eating has been, even in my own work.

What really trips up my clients, readers (and myself) has not been a lack of knowledge about what constitutes a healthy diet; it has been how to actually ensure we put that knowledge into practice in the midst of our hectic lives. We know we need to eat multiple times every day and it's important for our health that we make our meals as nourishing as possible – which inevitably means shopping, preparing and cooking whole food ingredients from scratch every day.

I totally understand how much of a challenge this might seem. As a nutrition professional, you probably think I should find it 'easy' – but I don't! The isolating period of the pandemic has only made this process harder, too, as it meant there was no respite from the need to provide all meals at home every single day. Over the past few years, I've found myself on a mission, trying to find ways to make the task of healthy eating easier and more efficient (and enjoyable). Ways to join the dots between wanting to eat well, and the everyday reality of putting that into practice. Importantly, I didn't want to focus on the food itself (or our willpower – which I think is in short supply for many of us right now).

Instead, I found myself focusing on a handful of practical but surprisingly influential things, such as: how our kitchen is equipped and arranged, and whether that supports or hinders cooking from scratch; how simple meal planning has the power to reduce the stress and mental load around choosing what to eat, not to mention food waste; how to navigate cost-effective food shopping when a giant industry of merchandising and marketing is specifically trying to tempt us away from whole food choices; and even how the way we eat can influence our digestive health and appetite. The list goes on!

Before we dive too deep into these topics, though, let me reassure you that this book is absolutely not about holding ourselves to some sort of organisational ideal where everything is always tidy, and the fridge is always arranged like a rainbow! This simply creates unnecessary pressure and makes us even more likely to fall off the bandwagon. Instead, I'd urge you to take from this book what resonates most – perhaps just one or two ideas at a time – and work with those until they come naturally. Then maybe take on board another couple of ideas. We don't have to do it all for big transformations to happen – consistency, not perfection, is what gets the best results.

What was perhaps most surprising about writing *The Organised Cook* is that, though I didn't realise this when I started, these steps are the same ones that I have been implementing with my clients for years! Almost all of my greatest success stories have begun with me turning up in a client's kitchen armed with containers, recipes and ready to use a bit of elbow grease. Within a couple of days, we'd have the kitchen sparkling and ship-shape, a fridge and freezer filled with portions of home-cooked meals, a clear menu plan and shopping list in place (we'd even go shopping together so I could teach them my healthy supermarket strategies and how to read food labels), alongside a load of back-up ideas for when life gets hectic and cooking becomes impossible. This process formed the solid foundation upon which a sustainable, healthy diet could be built. So I know that it really works, not just for me, but for anyone who wants to eat well, whatever kind of a kitchen you have.

Whether cooking for one, or for a huge crowd, I can't wait to go on this life-changing journey with you, saving time, money, stress and waste while finding a consistently joyful way to eat well for life.

Happy organising!

Amelia x

PART ONE

Organise

ORGANISE YOUR SPACE

If we pause to think for a moment about where a healthy diet fundamentally comes from, we quickly realise the importance that our kitchen plays in the health of ourselves and our families.

And yet, how often in everything written about healthy eating, is it assumed that we already have an efficient kitchen, as well as the knowledge, equipment and skills needed to keep churning out nourishing meal after nourishing meal?

When kitchens *are* discussed, it's mostly in the context of design and aesthetics, rather than functionality. But setting up our kitchen space to be as convenient and supportive to our health as possible is a massive win when it comes to eating well.

This part of the healthy-eating puzzle has been long overlooked, in my opinion. Yet it is something I have always addressed with my long-term clients and is something I hope I can help you with in this chapter.

To start, I want to bust a pervasive myth. An effective kitchen has nothing to do with how big or fancy it is, whether it's new or decades old, or even how much storage or work space there is. These things really don't matter when it comes to eating well. What matters is the food and drink we bring into our kitchens, how we organise it, and how we make best use of our space and equipment to consistently cook nourishing meals from scratch.

I've seen some incredibly busy commercial kitchens pumping out food from a space half the size of the average home kitchen. What chefs do particularly well is to make their limited spaces clean, clear and well-organised, and to kit them out with a useful 'capsule collection' of effective tools, store-cupboard staples and fresh produce. As home cooks, we can take inspiration from this professional-grade organisation to make our own cooking as efficient and enjoyable as possible.

'It's not about what we have, but how we organise and use it.'

Some of you will already be experienced and confident in the kitchen, so what I'm about to share might seem obvious common sense. If you're already doing lots of it, then you're off to a great start. But, for those of you who might feel a little less confident in the kitchen but who want to eat more economically and healthily, I'm going to go through it all systematically. Chances are there are still some areas you might not have considered before, or ways of thinking that might offer new insights and ideas.

We're going to start with a great big satisfying sort out, declutter and restock. We'll be going through every cupboard, drawer and hidden corner of your kitchen, and we'll be methodical about what to keep, what can be donated and what needs to be repaired, recycled, or responsibly disposed of. We will then put everything back together in the most efficient and healthy way possible, according to the space available, and hopefully we will arrive at the end of this chapter with a kitchen that is perfectly set-up for years of healthy cooking.

This stage will take a little bit of time and work. But, rest assured, you will reap the benefits in the future – in terms of time, money, nutrition and probably even better health.

THE THREE 'U'S TOOL

The Three 'U's help us to check that every item in the kitchen earns its place by being **Useful, Used** or still **Useable.** We will use this tool as we go through each area of the kitchen. It's such a satisfying and helpful process.

Is it Useful? Does it contribute to your cooking or kitchen storage, or to making meal preparation easier, more efficient, joyful or effective? Is it an ingredient that you like, need or use?

If it is not Useful, it doesn't deserve space in the kitchen. We often hold on to items that aren't really useful any more – things like rusty peelers, blunt knives, ancient appliances and bits and pieces that have accrued over the years (hello, five mini graters from Christmas crackers). If something isn't useful, it's time to donate, recycle or dispose of it responsibly.

Is it Used? Is it a piece of kit that has been used at least a few times in the last year and will continue to be used? Is it an ingredient you will actually cook with?

If it is not Used, it doesn't deserve space in the kitchen. If you can't bear to part with an item, or you will use it very occasionally (i.e., Christmas tableware or other sentimental items), then keep it, but move the item into a labelled container and store it away from the kitchen, such as in the garage, attic, cupboard or under a bed. This can free up space in the kitchen. If you can let it go, it's time to donate, recycle or dispose of it responsibly.

Is it Useable? Is it in a good state of repair? Does it fulfil its function efficiently? Is it still good to eat and is it within its use-by date?

If it is no longer Useable, consider repairing, re-sharpening or repurposing, if possible. If not, dispose of the item responsibly. Look for local Repair Cafés if you need help fixing broken appliances or utensils; these are a brilliant initiative to minimise waste. Dispose of any food that is no longer good to eat in a responsible way, recycling the packaging as far as possible.

Remember, it is not about what we have, but how we use it. An organised tiny kitchen is *always* better in terms of supporting our health goals than a super-smart and enormous kitchen that doesn't function on a practical level.

THE STEP-BY-STEP GUIDE

I try to go through the following steps every year or so, often in spring or in the lead-up to a big party. That way, I can maintain and edit the culinary systems I have in place to match my cooking challenges and goals, as well as avoiding it all getting too messed up again.

STEP 1: COOKING EQUIPMENT

Edit and declutter

Let's start by sorting through all the cooking equipment, appliances and storage containers. On the opposite page I have shared a list of what I feel are the most essential items of cooking kit, so it might be helpful to check that, if you aren't sure what you do and don't need in your kitchen.

There are two ways to do this:

1. Get every last thing out of the cupboards and off your shelves and onto the floor or worktops. This works well if you have the space (physical, emotional and mental) and time to do it all at once. Get a good playlist or podcast going in the background.

2. Go drawer-by-drawer and cupboard-by-cupboard over time. This is a more realistic approach for many of us and it can help to gradually build up your confidence and sense of satisfaction with each area sorted.

> **TIP:** *If you find letting go of things (or organisation generally) a difficult process, then the second approach is definitely the one I'd recommend. Schedule a date and time to make a start, set a timer for 30 minutes, and take it in bitesize chunks. It might be nice to enlist a friend or family member to do a bit with you, too.*

Whichever way you choose to tackle the kitchen organisation process, it's worth working through everything you've got, piece by piece, deciding if each item fulfils at least one of the Three 'U's.

What do we really need?

Here's a list of the basic, everyday kit and utensils I think a kitchen needs to make nutritious food from scratch. All these items need to be in good working order. They're mostly inexpensive and charity shops or second-hand shops offer a goldmine of great-quality used kitchen equipment, glassware, cutlery and crockery, if you need any extra bits and pieces. Good basic kit really will transform how easy and enjoyable it is for you to cook.

Essential kitchen kit

Of course, what I feel is 'essential' may well differ from what you find essential and will also change according to the cuisine or types of dishes you most often cook. However, for anyone interested in knowing what I use most – and therefore what my recipes most often call for – here goes:

'Great organisation needs enough space to breathe'

1. **Chopping board(s)** A solid wooden board can also double as a serving platter. I'd recommend keeping a separate board for raw meat and fish (ideally dishwasher safe).

2. **Small preparing knife (7.5cm/3in blade) and small serrated knife** Useful for the majority of vegetable prep. Victorinox make some of the best, in my experience. A knife sharpener is also essential, as a blunt knife is one of the most dangerous – and useless – tools in the kitchen.

3. **Chef's knife (20cm/8in blade)** Great for chopping herbs and larger vegetables and it can double up as a carving knife.

4. **Bread knife** As most homemade or minimally processed bread doesn't come pre-sliced, it's important to have a knife that can slice bread effectively.

5. **Kitchen scissors**

6. **Whisk** Buy a silicone one if you want to avoid scratching pans.

7. **Sieve** A metal sieve lasts longer and can double up as a colander.

8. **Saucepans** Ideally, aim to have one small, two medium and one large pan, all with lids, and a steamer, too. Good-quality pans are an investment, but should last many decades. Find ones with a heavy base, as this makes a huge difference to how they distribute heat – and prevents food burning in annoying areas on the bottom of the pan. Stainless steel, cast iron or enamel pans are what I prefer to use. I steer clear of aluminium, non-stick and antique copper pans, as they can all potentially leach metals or chemicals into food, and the health effects of this are uncertain (for example, as the non-stick coating gets scratched and exposed to repeated heat and washing). Double check that any new pans are compatible with an induction hob, if you have one.

TIP: *Use three cardboard boxes as you declutter so you can easily sort items into Donate, Recycle, Repair.*

9. **Sauté pan or frying pan** I use mine for everything from simple pasta sauces to pancakes, stir-fries and falafel. I'd opt for a heavy-bottomed pan, ideally with a lid, in uncoated stainless steel or cast iron.

10. **Wooden spoons**

11. **Fish slice** Far better than thick spatulas that merely push food around, rather than neatly getting underneath it.

12. **Box grater** If yours is blunt, replace it.

13. **A sharp vegetable peeler (or three)** Having a blunt peeler adds hours to food preparation time each month, so for a few pounds it's worth investing in a good a peeler. Also, if you constantly find yourself needing to grab it out of the dishwasher or sink, please give yourself the gift of a spare peeler or two.

14. **Stick blender** Handy for making soups, sauces and smoothies, and much cheaper (and smaller) than a stand-alone blender.

15. **Tea towels** Find ones that make you feel happy when you look at them (same goes for aprons).

16. **Tongs** A heatproof extension of your fingers.

17. **Roasting tray** I prefer stainless-steel or enamel trays. If you've got the budget and space, look for a small-medium and a large one (check they will fit inside your oven first).

Nice-to-have kitchen kit

There are lots of additional bits and pieces that you can add to these essentials, if you choose to. The difference here is that I don't think they are necessarily *critical* for an effective working kitchen, but are nice to have and can offer some time savings, if space and budget allow. Feel free to move things between lists if you know certain items are essential in your own kitchen.

1. **Food processor** Useful for making hummus and other dips, pesto, salsa, pastry, homemade burgers and for grating salads and coleslaws – amongst many other things. I have a Magimix food processor that has been a trusted friend for the best part of ten years and is still going strong.

2. **Glass storage containers** Great for packed lunches, picnics, snacks, leftovers, batch cooking and more. I use mine every single day. I have a stack of Pyrex (heatproof) glass containers with airtight lids, alongside a stash of clean jam jars and storage jars. I recommend glass over plastic, where possible, to avoid food being exposed to potentially disruptive materials in plastic. Plus, it's see-through, so you know immediately what's inside. But don't worry too

much if you already have plastic. Just try to avoid heating food in plastic containers (including in the microwave). Instead, decant into a glass or ceramic bowl before heating.

3. **Lemon press** Makes squeezing lemons easy – for drizzling over dishes or for making dressings.

4. **Measuring jug**

5. **Mixing bowls** A few different-sized metal bowls that are lightweight, easy to clean and heat tolerant are very useful. They can also double up as a rubbish bowl when preparing ingredients, keeping work surfaces clean and clear.

6. **Weighing scales** Electronic scales can be zeroed before adding new ingredients to the same bowl (which saves on washing up).

7. **Microplane grater** Handy for zesting citrus and grating garlic, ginger, Parmesan and nutmeg. It's also easier to clean than a box grater and is often a bit sharper.

8. **Oven dishes (ceramic)**

9. **Cast-iron casserole dish** Good for things as diverse as stews, soups, casseroles, roasting chickens and baking bread. I have a few from Le Creuset, although various places do their own versions. They are definitely an investment, but they'll last forever if well looked after, and are brilliant at distributing and holding heat. If you choose just one, go for a shallow, lidded casserole, as it's probably the most versatile.

10. **Serving dishes and bowls**

11. **Salad servers**

12. **Aprons**

13. **Speakers / radio** Because music is such a good accompaniment to cooking.

14. **Slow-cooker** If you don't have much time or energy to cook in the evenings, a slow-cooker can be a complete game-changer. They cost around £30 (about the same as a takeaway) and they make batch cooking a breeze. They're about the size of a large casserole dish – throw in double the quantity of ingredients you need for a recipe and freeze or refrigerate the extra portions for another day.

Deep clean

Before putting everything you want to keep back again, deep clean all your now-empty cupboards, drawers and shelves. It's surprisingly satisfying to get rid of the random crumbs that have gathered in the cutlery tray, unusual stains from the tin cupboard and scuffs from the saucepan drawer. See more about cleaning in the Kitchen Cleaning Tips and Tricks section on pages 76–9.

Conjuring up a little more space

Now is also the time to optimise your storage spaces. There is often a lot of unused 'dead' space in cupboards and drawers that can be brought back into use with a little thought or the odd clever storage solution.

Having systems in place that give every item its own 'home' (rather than balancing it on a teetering pile) makes maintaining a slick kitchen SO much easier. Aim for everything to have its own dedicated place and space in containers, baskets or shelves so that they are easy to find when in the middle of cooking.

TIP: *If there's a cupboard next to your oven, some stick-on hooks can be useful to hang oven gloves and towels inside of the door.*

Here are a few ideas to get you started:

- If possible, adjust the shelves inside your cupboards to match your storage requirements, possibly even adding extra shelves if there's space. Most kitchen cupboards let you do this relatively easily with adjustable pegs.

- A stepped shelf organiser, an adjustable cupboard rack for storing baking trays or chopping boards vertically, shelf or drawer dividers and under-shelf storage baskets can all be helpful.

- A spinning turntable for oils, vinegars and other condiments can be useful, if you have the space. It stops flavour-boosting ingredients from languishing at the back of the cupboard.

- Use trays, baskets or boxes for storing similar types of products together. For example, I like to group oils and vinegars together, or sauces and condiments. They're also helpful for storing bulky goods. Make sure you label them clearly.

- If you're struggling for cupboard space, try hanging saucepans or cooking utensils on hooks above the oven or work surface. This also solves the problem of having to pull every last stacked pan and lid out to get the single one you're after.

- Hook-on cupboard door shelves are handy for storing spices or other small items.

- A saucepan lid holder helps to keep lids vertically stacked and easily accessible (though, I personally prefer to keep my lids with my pans – it just depends on how much space you have).

- In-drawer wooden knife blocks help keep kitchen knives safely organised. You could also try a magnetic knife strip on the wall to keep surfaces clutter free.

Right things, right place

The next step is all about ensuring that the right things are put back in the right place and sorted the right way.

We (understandably) have a tendency not to think things through very hard when we first move into a new home. We unpack our boxes, rushing to get everything put away as quickly as possible, and rarely go back to think about whether we have established the most efficient layout.

I ended up reorganising my kitchen two years after I moved into our house, when I realised that I had put the things we use the most – our cutlery, plates and saucepans – in the set of drawers furthest away from where I need them. So don't forget that it's OK to re-jig your space at any time to make it work in the best way possible for you and your family.

Here are the groupings I use to help create a logical order in my kitchen. Please adapt these to suit your needs. I try to keep the items within each grouping in roughly the same area of the kitchen (perhaps in one cupboard, or over a couple of side-by-side drawers, for example), and assign that area according to where I am most likely to need and use them:

- **Everyday food preparation equipment** – chopping boards, knives, mixing bowls, peelers – or the things I use the most (pretty much every day). I prioritise keeping these items within easy reach, in the most accessible location and close to my Golden Work Space (more on this on page 21).

- **Cooking utensils, saucepans, casseroles, oven trays and roasting tins** – basically, all the things that get hot. I keep my most-used cooking utensils, such as tongs, a fish slice / spatula and wooden spoons, in a large pot next to my hob as I need to be able to reach them with one hand, while my other is usually holding a hot pan or dish. Utensils that are used less frequently can be kept in a drawer close by or hung on hooks behind the hob. I keep saucepans and oven trays in the drawers next to the oven, or they can be hung behind the hob.

- **Everyday condiments** – I keep a small tray of olive oil, salt, pepper, soy sauce, mustard and vinegars next to my hob, as I use these frequently when cooking and don't want to waste time getting them out of a cupboard.

- **Crockery, cutlery and glasses** – store your everyday plates, bowls, glasses and cutlery in the cupboard (or shelves) closest to your dishwasher or drying rack, if possible.

- **Items used less frequently** – serving dishes, plates, occasional glasses etc. These can then be stored in less accessible places. Perhaps not even in the kitchen, if space is short.

TIP: *After you have decluttered, take the time to measure up before you buy any storage items (especially baskets or containers).*

- **Appliances and electrical goods** – I have five appliances out on my worktops: kettle, coffee machine, toaster, blender and food processor. I use these appliances day-in, day-out and find them to be great time-savers, so they more than earn their worktop space. I know that I'd use the blender or processor far less often if I had to drag them out of the back of the cupboard every time I wanted to whip up some hummus, for example. So, I'd suggest doing the same, if you can. Mini versions are available if you don't have space for the larger ones. If you do have additional appliances that you use less frequently, store them in cupboards and bring them out as required. But remember to refer back to the Three 'U's on page 11 if you're not sure you'll *actually* use them…

- **Food storage and containers** – empty tubs, containers, jars, bags and wraps etc. I am a stickler for keeping lids attached to their containers rather than storing them separately. This does depend on the space you have, but it is worth it, if you can. Get rid of all the random lids that don't have a home.

- **Textiles** – tea towels, aprons, table linens etc. I also have a pile of little flannels that I keep as re-usable kitchen towels. They're easily washable and are as great for sticky faces and hands as they are for work surfaces and spills. I keep mine in a drawer underneath the cooking utensils as that's where I have space, but stash yours anywhere convenient. By the sink or cooker would be ideal.

- **Cleaning supplies** – washing-up liquid, soap, surface cleaners, sponges, dishwasher tablets etc. I keep these under the sink. If you have young children, you might need to use a cupboard lock or keep them in a high cupboard, out of reach.

- **Bins** – compost, recycling etc. I have a multi-bin, with two compartments for recycling and general waste, but a few separate, clearly labelled storage boxes can also work (so you can sort out your recycling as you go). I also have a compost bucket as we compost our own material, but if composting isn't an option, you could enquire if there are local food waste bins near you. Try to keep these as close to your main preparation area as possible. You're inevitably going to have packaging, compost and food waste to dispose of as you prepare food. It's much easier to keep the work area clean and sort the waste out appropriately if all the various bins are easy to reach.

You might have additional categories that I haven't mentioned here, such as baking supplies, children's items, or speciality cooking equipment. Simply think about how often you need / use them, and place them accordingly.

If after this process you feel that you still need to find more storage space in your kitchen, see if you can add some extra shelves – either attached to the wall or freestanding. As they are not as deep as cupboards, shelves maintain more of a sense of space, while still helping to keep your work surfaces clear. You might even be able squeeze them into places that are otherwise unused (on top of cupboards, over the fridge or doorways, above the sink etc.). They do tend to need more cleaning than cupboards, though, as cooking steam and fat accumulates. I use my shelves for glasses, cookbooks, jars of dried goods, plates, bowls and serving dishes.

Define and declutter your Golden Work Space

A final useful step is to define your Golden Work Space. This is the area where you tend to do most of the food preparation. The place where you naturally find yourself standing to chop, mix and prepare, and where 90% of the output of your kitchen is likely to come from.

Remove worktop appliances, random jars or containers and clutter from this zone and give it a good clean. Keep knives, chopping boards and saucepans as close to hand as possible. From now on, try to keep this Golden Work Space as clean and clutter-free as possible. Your time spent cooking will feel infinitely less stressful as a result.

A note on cookbooks: I adore cookbooks and, as someone who writes them, I totally under-stand how much work goes into creating them. I also love to browse them, and will cling to favourites as deeply sentimental items, holding as they do, so many memories of joyful family feasts and late-night frivolity with friends. However, if you're anything like me, it can get a little overwhelming if you have too many books. All those uncooked and untasted recipes, gathering dust, making me feel guilty for not getting around to making them yet. So, as you go through the kitchen equipment, also take a moment to go through your cookbooks. Any books that you no longer use, want or feel aligned to can be given away or donated to a charity shop for someone else to enjoy.

If you have limited shelf space in your kitchen, you could put your cookbooks elsewhere in your home, and rotate a small selection of the best seasonal books through your kitchen. This not only reduces clutter, but might also encourage you to try out a few new recipes and cook what is in season.

STEP 2: DRIED / STORE-CUPBOARD FOODS

Edit and declutter

Well done for getting this far. I hope you have found it as satisfying as I do. Organising your kitchen equipment can be quite cathartic and hopefully you have freed up a little extra kitchen space. Don't worry if you've also found it overwhelming and tiring. Going through a lifetime of accumulated 'stuff' can be exhausting. Take your time – it will be worth it in the end.

Now our next step is to go through all the dried goods, tins and store-cupboard ingredients: packets, oils, condiments, spices, herbs, grains, pasta, cereals, baking products and the rest. I assume that you have some store-cupboard foods to sort out! It might be stating the obvious, but an empty kitchen doesn't encourage us to eat better (or less). Instead, it means we come to rely on convenience foods and takeaways, since cooking any meal would necessitate going shopping. I worked with a couple of clients who had a rule never to keep food in the house and only shop as and when they needed it (in their case so they didn't overeat). But it meant that meals weren't well planned and they'd end up overeating from getting hungry. If building up a store-cupboard supply is a budget issue, take a look on pages 62–6 for some helpful tips.

For this step, I would really recommend getting everything out and trying to sort through it in one go. It's so helpful to see everything all together. If that's not realistic, though, take it one shelf or cupboard at a time.

HEALTHY-EATING TIP: *While clearing out the food cupboards, gather any food stored elsewhere in the house: desks, bedrooms, the car etc. From now on, try to store food only in the kitchen. From my experience supporting clients through this process, food kept outside of the kitchen tends to be snack food, sweets or chocolate – foods that may be fun but aren't necessarily supportive to our health and wellbeing. The easier these sorts of foods are to reach for, the more likely we are to do just that. The simple act of having to stand up and walk to get a snack can reduce the temptation.*

1. Go through all the food items you've gathered and check they are still within the use-by date and haven't spoiled. Dispose of anything that has, rinsing and recycling any containers as necessary.

2. Sort through what's left and use the Three 'U's on page 11 to help decide whether or not you want or need to keep it.

3. Remove additional or excess outer packaging, such as cardboard boxes around multi-packs, as they just take up space (unless it's necessary to keep them for nutrition or ingredient / allergen information).

4. If you have multiple opened packets of the same dried or long-lasting food (such as rice, flour, seeds, nuts, pasta, snacks etc.) put them into one storage container (I find this so satisfying).

5. Finally, donate any unwanted food that is unopened, good to eat and within date and dispose responsibly of anything you no longer wish to keep. What's left should just be the goods that you want and are in date.

The list of store-cupboard ingredients opposite is what I try to keep on hand. The staples form the foundation of many quick and easy meals, so having a small stock of them in the kitchen is really helpful and definitely time-saving. The nice-to-haves offer some time-saving shortcuts or are just great to have to hand, but are not essential to creating everyday healthy, cost-effective meals.

Store-cupboard staples

Bread: Rye, sourdough, wholegrain or gluten-free
Dried herbs and spices
Dried lentils
Flours: plain and self-raising (gluten-free, if necessary)
Oats
Olive oil: I use a light olive oil for cooking, and extra-virgin olive oil for drizzling and dressing.
Pasta: Brown, spelt, red lentil or chickpea
Rice: Brown or wild
Seeds, nuts, nut butters and tahini
Stock or bouillon powder
Tinned coconut milk
Tinned or jarred pulses: chickpeas, black beans, butter beans and cannellini beans
Tinned or jarred tomatoes or tomato passata
Tinned or jarred fish: Tuna, sardines and anchovies
Vinegar: Apple cider or white wine

Store-cupboard nice-to-haves

Cacao / cocoa powder or dark chocolate (ideally >85% cocoa content)
Cooked lentil pouches – such a great time-saver
Dried fruit
Garlic purée
Honey, maple syrup or brown sugar
Jarred roasted peppers and preserved lemons
Jarred olives, sun-dried tomatoes or artichoke hearts
Other condiments: miso and harissa
Other flours: gram, spelt and buckwheat
Other oils: sesame, avocado, coconut
Other vinegars: balsamic, sherry, red wine
Quinoa / cooked quinoa pouches
Tinned or jarred vegetables: sweetcorn and pickles
Tomato purée

HEALTHY-EATING TIP: *Know your weaknesses. Are there one or two types of food that you can't stop eating when you begin? For one of my team members, it's dried fruit. For me, it's salty crisps. One of the simplest and least effortful ways of combatting this is to not have these foods in the house. I know that might seem harsh, but it's honestly sometimes the easiest option. Remember – we can store foods at the store. We don't have to store them in our homes. If this isn't possible (perhaps they are necessary for a family member), place such items in opaque containers out of reach and sight.*

Right foods, right place

Now the editing and cleaning is complete, the next stage is to arrange all the store-cupboard foods into categories, just as we did for cooking equipment. How exactly you choose to do this will depend quite a bit on personal preference, but the critical factor is to choose a system that works for you and is one that you, and any people living with you, can maintain.

Why bother with this process? There are three very good reasons.

- It helps us keep an eye on 'stock'. If all the tins of tomatoes are kept in one place, for example, then we know at a glance how many are left. If they're scattered around different shelves or cupboards, we'd have to go through everything to know what we have. This takes time and increases the chance of food waste.

- It sparks ideas. We've all had evenings where we open the kitchen cupboard in the hope of getting inspiration. It's much more likely to work if those foods are sorted into vaguely logical categories rather than being one chaotic mess.

- It can help to support healthier food choices. Keep whole foods and healthy ingredients at eye level and within easy reach. This could include tinned vegetables or fish, pulses, wholegrains, olive oil, herbs and spices, for example. However, keep snack foods, processed foods and anything you don't want to eat as often in opaque containers above or below eye level, or at the back of the cupboard. Making them awkward to access can help to create enough of a subconscious hurdle that we are less likely to reach for them out of habit. Out of sight, out of mind.

It doesn't really matter in terms of our health exactly *which* categorisation system you use. The key is for it to be logical to you, to be consistent, and to keep in mind how much space you have available (as it's helpful to keep the entire category together in one place, if possible, rather than splitting up similar items between different cupboards or areas).

Some people like to categorise based on meals of the day – breakfast foods, lunch foods, snacks, dinners etc. Some by ingredient – pulses, grains, baking ingredients, spices etc. Some by flavour profile. Once you've decided which system works best for you, designate each category a zone, shelf or area of the kitchen, in a way that feels most logical.

'Make what's good for us easy to see and easy to reach, and what's less healthy for us harder to see and harder to reach. It's a simple but effective strategy to eat more healthily without trying.'

Just try to remember here that *function comes before appearance*. If you focus too much on making your cupboards or shelves look beautiful, they won't function properly and the organisation won't last, or will take an enormous amount of effort to maintain. As much as I'd love to colour co-ordinate my cupboards, it just isn't practical. If, however, you start with function, you can always make it look lovely later (perhaps with baskets, labels, containers etc.).

To decant or not to decant?

Decanting dried foods into clear containers is something I have done for a long while, and long before social media made it 'trendy'. It's not for everyone, though, so here are a few pros and cons to consider before investing in containers:

Pros:

- Easy to see what you have in stock.

- Visual prompt to use a variety of ingredients in your cooking.

- Aesthetically pleasing – avoids acres of half-opened packets and lots of spillage when rummaging around for things.

- Can help food last longer.

- Usually stackable.

- Good for open storage / shelves.

- May save money as you can buy ingredients in bulk.

Cons:

- Containers can be expensive to buy.

- Time consuming to decant everything and maintain good stock rotation.

- Removes use-by dates / ingredients / nutrition / instructions from labels (which can be problematic with food allergies, for example).

- If stored in a see-through container and is not a health food, it could be a visual prompt to eat more of it (sweets, biscuits, for example).

- Need to be consistent with the foods you buy – or you'll end up needing a lot of containers.

I use glass jars for bulkier items and old jam jars (washed thoroughly and labels removed) for less bulky things, like spices, herbs, seeds etc. You can buy specific, clear food storage containers, many of which are square and stackable – optimising efficient use of space – but they tend to be more expensive.

Label your containers well

The key to successful decanting is to label well.

If you are bothered about the appearance of your label, just do what I do and stick them underneath. Otherwise, there are plenty of beautiful labels available online – and blackboard stickers which you can write on in chalk can look nice. If you're not overly fussed about what your labels look like, write on a strip of masking tape with a Sharpie – the masking tape is easy to remove and replace if you change the contents of the container. It is also helpful to write the use-by date.

I find decanting really useful and don't mind the few minutes it takes when I unpack the shopping. I store my jars on open shelves so I can see instantly what I have, and as almost everything I store in these containers is a whole food, wholegrain or otherwise nourishing ingredient, it's a great visual prompt to spark my imagination for healthy meals. It also allows me to buy dried goods in bulk, which is helpful from a budget and sustainability perspective. And I think they look pretty, too.

A note on food left out…

Not all food is kept behind cupboard doors or inside fridges and freezers. Some of it is out on display – perhaps on open shelves or the worktop for instance. That might be because we're short on space, or just the way we like to set up our kitchens.

If what's out and visible are things like seasonal fruits, vegetables or containers of dried whole foods, then, chances are, this will help to support healthy cooking and food choices. If, however, what's on display are biscuit or cake tins, packaged breakfast cereals, packets and containers of other snack or ultra-processed foods, then it's going to be much harder for us (and potentially our family members) to resist the temptation of grazing on them. We're likely to want them more often and then, perhaps, will have to rely on our willpower to keep things in moderation – which is challenging and often not very effective.

So remember, try to keep any foods that you are intending or aiming to eat more of out on display, and hide away those you'd like to eat less often. Perhaps try putting the biscuit tin inside a cupboard, decanting cereals into opaque containers, and moving snack foods out of your line of vision. And don't keep the biscuit tin near the kettle – there's no better prompt to eat a biscuit every time you make a hot drink, than seeing them right there in front of you!

STEP 3: THE FRIDGE

It's time to tackle the fridge, the last of these big organising jobs. You're nearly there.

A well-organised fridge with a logical system of food storage and display can help to tackle waste and save us money, as well as making cooking nourishing food from scratch a far simpler task.

The fridge is not supposed to be a place where food goes to be forgotten. According to the Love Food Hate Waste campaign in the UK, 3.1 million glasses of milk are poured away daily, and 70% of the food that is wasted is done so in our homes, costing the average family of four £60 a month. Or £720 a year. That's a lot of waste.

One of the key culprits is the fridge. Or rather, I should say, a poorly organised fridge.

Let's cover some basics first:

- A fridge should be kept between 3-5°C. Some fridges have their own thermometers, but you can buy in-fridge ones cheaply online if your fridge is older or you need a more accurate reading. The average UK fridge is reportedly set to 7°C, which means that food is likely to perish faster, so it's definitely worth checking.

- Try not to overcrowd the fridge. Cool air needs to be able to circulate around refrigerated food to keep it cold. An over-stocked fridge can create warmer spots that increase the risk of spoilage. However, keeping it relatively full helps to maintain a constant cool temperature. It's a bit of a Goldilocks situation – not too much, not too little.

- Before every shopping trip, take a quick look through the fridge and see what's hiding in there, so you don't inadvertently buy twice. Take a photo with your phone so you can refer back to it while you're in the store, if you might find this helpful.

- Check the fridge seals. If the seal is damaged or split it might allow cold air to escape, making the fridge work extra hard to stay cool. These can be replaced. Clean the seals regularly, too. It's amazing and revolting to see what accumulates in there!

- Try to keep the fridge door shut as much as possible. Once the door has been opened for a while, it can take hours for the interior to cool down fully again.

- Use trays, baskets and containers to keep items of a similar nature together. Label each container clearly so the system is easy to maintain for whoever is unpacking the shopping or using the fridge.

- Keep a few clip-lock containers to hand for cheeses and other potentially pungent items (half a leftover onion or a banana, for example). Otherwise, they can taint the flavour of everything in the fridge.

Edit and declutter

Once again, we want to start the editing and decluttering process by getting everything out of the fridge, checking the use-by dates, and disposing of anything that is out of date, has been open too long and we know we're not going to eat, or that has spoiled. Don't forget to refer back to the Three 'U's, on page 11 if you find it helpful.

Deep clean

Give the fridge a good, deep clean (including the shelves, seals and drains). Check any water filters, if you have them. See page 76 for fridge cleaning tips.

Fix your fridge door

Before we dive into re-stocking the fridge, check the door opens in the most efficient way. The doors on most fridges and freezers can be adjusted to open to the left or to the right (check the instruction manual to see if this applies to yours, and how to do it). It is a pet peeve of mine to see a fridge door that opens the wrong way, so that you have to walk around it to get the contents of the fridge to the main work surface.

Right foods, right place

As with our store cupboards, there are significant benefits to organising our fridges efficiently for supporting optimum nutrition and reducing food waste (and therefore saving money). Here's the system I use that helps to achieve both at the same time. It's been life-changing.

TIP: *Keep any meat, fish or other highly perishable foods in a cool box or cool bag with ice packs as you go through this process, so they aren't out of the fridge for too long. Remember to keep raw meat / fish separate from other foods as you do so.*

TOP SHELF

Store your dairy (cheese, butter, yoghurt etc.) at the top of the fridge.

HEALTHY-EATING TIP: *Cheese freezes well, so if you want to save money by buying in bulk or you want to limit the amount of cheese you eat each week, simply portion it up and wrap it tightly in parchment paper. Place some in the fridge and the remainder in the freezer.*

Leftovers should also be kept on the top shelf in clear (ideally glass) containers with airtight lids. Keeping them at eye level helps us remember they are there, and using clear containers makes it really obvious what it is we have to finish up. Nothing languishes more readily than a small, covered bowl of leftovers pushed right to the back of the fridge.

It is also important to decant leftover tinned food, as storing open tins can leave foods with a metallic taste.

MIDDLE SHELF

Keep fresh vegetables at eye level. This is perhaps a little controversial as, traditionally, vegetables would be stored in the crisper drawers to maintain humidity and freshness. I do store salad leaves in the drawers, as I find these go off first and therefore benefit from being stored there. However, in terms of optimising *nutrition*, I find that putting fresh vegetables front and centre of the fridge is massively helpful in encouraging us to eat more of them, and therefore reducing the risk that they'll stay hidden at the back of the crisper drawers and go off before we have a chance to eat them.

I also like being able to see which vegetables I have to hand. I find this method of storing them prompts me to include more variety in my meals.

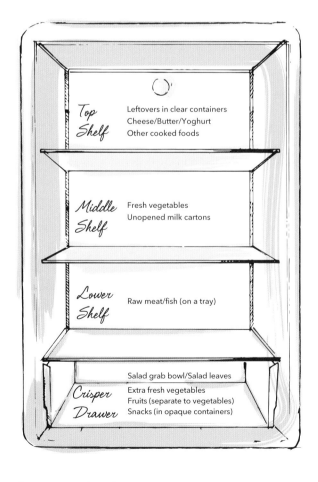

Top Shelf
Leftovers in clear containers
Cheese/Butter/Yoghurt
Other cooked foods

Middle Shelf
Fresh vegetables
Unopened milk cartons

Lower Shelf
Raw meat/fish (on a tray)

Crisper Drawer
Salad grab bowl/Salad leaves
Extra fresh vegetables
Fruits (separate to vegetables)
Snacks (in opaque containers)

LOWER SHELF

Raw meat and fish should always go on the lowest shelf. This solves the issue of it potentially dripping onto, and contaminating, other foods. Place the raw meat or fish in a tray or container to help contain any leaks and to make cleaning easier.

CRISPER DRAWERS

I generally keep a salad spinner bowl or bag of ready-washed, undressed salad leaves in my crisper drawer. I call it my 'grab salad', as it makes adding green leaves to any meal quick and easy (and is a very obvious visual reminder to do so). I try to have three portions of green vegetables every day, so this strategy really helps to achieve that nutritional goal.

However, if you don't get through quite as much salad as I do, a good way to help leaves last longer (especially spinach) is to place a clean piece of kitchen paper into a sealed bag alongside the leaves. This absorbs any excess moisture and really helps them to last.

Additional fresh vegetables (that don't fit on the middle shelf, or that you want to keep for later in the week) will also go in the crisper drawers. A good way to extend the life of lots of vegetables is to wrap them in a damp, clean tea towel. It works particularly well for carrots, celery and cucumbers.

I try, where possible, to keep fruit separate to vegetables. Most of our fruit is kept out of the fridge and in a fruit bowl, except for berries or very ripe fruit that needs to be kept cool to reduce the risk of spoilage. I never put bananas in the fridge, as it turns them black and they can taint other food.

HEALTHY-EATING TIP: *I look out for seasonal berries going on sale in supermarkets and freeze them along with my own homegrown (or foraged) ones. That way I can build up a stash of antioxidant-rich berries in the freezer to tide me over the winter – a moment of captured summer sunshine that always feels such a treat in the darkest, dampest months.*

If you want to keep berries fresher for longer, it can be really helpful to give them a vinegar rinse before storing them. They tend to be one of the more expensive foods to buy, so minimising the risk of food waste is important. Don't worry – they don't end up tasting of vinegar:

1. Fill a small bowl with cold water and add 4 tablespoons of white or apple cider vinegar. Add the berries and leave them to soak for 5 minutes.

2. Rinse the berries well under cold running water and discard the vinegar water.

3. Spread the berries out to dry completely (on a clean tea towel or in a salad spinner bowl). Any dampness will increase their likelihood of going off.

4. Put the dry berries in an airtight container and store in the fridge.

Snacks, desserts and occasional foods should also be stored in the crisper drawers. It can be helpful to keep these snacks in opaque containers, away from direct line of vision, ideally at the back of the drawers. This little additional inconvenience and lack of visual prompt can help to reduce how often we are reminded about, and therefore want to eat, these foods. It can be a particularly helpful trick if we need to keep snack foods for other members of the family, but would rather not be constantly prompted to eat them ourselves!

FRIDGE DOOR

The fridge door is generally the warmest place in the fridge, so it isn't ideal for storing leftovers or unopened milk, which both prefer a consistent, lower temperature. Things that do store well in the fridge door include:

- Condiments – as these usually contain natural preservatives, such as vinegar, so are happier in the slightly warmer temperature.

- Fresh herbs – unwrap them from their plastic, trim the stems and place in a glass or jar of water. If you don't have space in the fridge door, then wrap them in damp kitchen paper and keep them in the crisper drawers. I adore using fresh herbs in my cooking, and they are the one thing that I think is worth growing if you've only got a little space (a windowsill or small balcony perhaps), as they're generally pretty easy to grow but expensive to buy from the supermarket.

- Asparagus – trim the ends and stick them upright in a glass of water and they'll stay fresher for longer.

- Water filter – for easily accessible, clean, cold tap water.

- Open milk or other cartons – if the cartons are too tall to store on the shelves.

Things that don't generally need to be stored in the fridge

This list is especially helpful if you're stuck for space in the fridge. While most foods will last longer if kept in the fridge, especially if they are perfectly ripe, if the food is a little under-ripe, or you don't have enough space, then the following are happy to be stored at room temperature:

- Avocados

- Bananas

- Apples and pears

- Citrus fruits (although, I generally keep lemons in the fridge, as I find they go off a lot quicker than oranges, grapefruit or satsumas. Try keeping them in a jar of water in the fridge for extra longevity.)

- Bread (if you don't eat much bread, slice it and freeze it as soon as you buy or bake it. Toast the frozen slices straight from the freezer as and when you want some.)

- Nectarines, peaches, plums and other stone fruit

- Mangos and pineapples

- Tomatoes are always more delicious eaten at room temperature, so take them out of the fridge a couple of hours before eating, if you do keep them in the fridge.

- Potatoes and sweet potatoes should be kept in a well-ventilated, dark, dry place. A wicker basket in a cupboard is ideal. Don't wash potatoes before storing them – the mud helps to keep them fresh for longer, and putting them away damp can encourage spoiling.

- Squash and pumpkins (so long as their skin is intact and they haven't been cut)

- Nuts, seeds and nut butters

- Soy sauce, vinegars, oils and other ambient condiments

- Onions and garlic should be stored in a basket, ideally, where air can circulate. Always unwrap any plastic before storing, as the plastic wrapping can encourage them to rot.

TIP: *Don't store basil in the fridge – it goes black and soggy. Store cut basil in a glass of water in a shady spot of the kitchen, or buy it as a plant.*

HEALTHY-EATING TIP: *I try to buy olive oil in dark bottles, as some of the beneficial nutrients that good olive oil contains are UV sensitive, and the darker bottles help to reduce any possible damage. It's a good idea, therefore, to keep your good oils out of direct sunlight, if possible.*

A note on drinks…

Storing alcohol or soft drinks outside of the fridge is one of the simplest tricks I know to help cut down how much we drink casually. A room-temperature juice, beer or glass of white wine is so much less appealing than a refreshingly cold one. And by the time we've waited for it to cool down, it's likely we'll no longer really want it anyway. Perhaps keep some sparkling or still water (flavoured with lemon, berries, rosemary, cucumber or mint, if you like) in the fridge to enjoy at the end of the day instead.

A note about leftovers

Using leftovers is key to making eating well a more time-efficient process, as we can eat twice or even three times from one cooking session. It's a no-brainer for busy people, and far cheaper than getting a takeaway. However, it relies upon our ability to store leftovers safely.

Ensure that food is cooled thoroughly before it goes into the fridge (never put hot / warm food into the fridge), and that the fridge is set to the correct temperature (3–5°C).

Try to put leftovers in the fridge as soon as they have cooled, ideally within two hours. You don't want it sitting around at room temperature for ages.

I recommend all leftovers are stored in reusable, airtight, clean containers (mine are glass with airtight lids). Label the container with what the food is and the date / day it was prepared.

'A kitchen should always be practical and efficient to use, and organising fridges, freezers and cupboards wisely will make your life easier in the long run.'
Mary Berry

TIP: *Find beautiful food containers that you love to store leftovers in, and take a few moments to make them look appetising. Even garnish them if you want. Alongside keeping them at eye level, you'll be amazed how much more you'll look forward to eating leftovers, and how much less like a sad afterthought they will seem, if you do so.*

Most leftovers are OK for three days, if stored correctly. If you want to store things for longer than this, I suggest freezing them in portions instead. Personally, I don't store leftover cooked rice, as it can contain spores of Bacillus cereus (a bacteria that causes food poisoning). If cooked rice is left standing, these spores can grow into bacteria and multiply or produce toxins. To err on the side of caution (and as rice is relatively inexpensive), I prefer to cook rice from fresh each time I want to enjoy it.

Use your nose and eyes – smell and look carefully at foods before eating them. Our senses can offer a lot of common sense when it comes to safe leftovers. Does it smell OK? Does it look OK? This shouldn't override the other tips here about storing safe leftovers, but is another layer of checking.

Heat leftover items thoroughly to piping hot before serving. If you have a food thermometer, you need to get it above 70°C for a minimum of 2 minutes. I generally don't re-heat foods more than once and I discard any leftovers second time around, although I try to avoid any waste like this with good meal planning (lots more on this in the PLAN chapter on pages 40-5).

MAINTAINING AN ORGANISED SPACE

We've been through the big sort-out process and, hopefully, the kitchen is now a strategically organised and efficient space from which to create nourishing meals with ease and speed. But life happens and real-world muddle and mess creep back in. What to do?

Firstly, let's just recognise that this is NORMAL and the sign of a well-loved space. It isn't possible to maintain a perfect kitchen all the time, especially if we are actually using it. A good working kitchen is not just for show – but we do want good systems in place, which can be achieved by a 'little and often' approach.

Take a look at my cleaning checklist on pages 77–9 for the essential regular cleaning tasks, as that goes a long way to maintaining a safe and efficient kitchen.

It can be helpful to set aside about half an hour each month to do a stock-check and mini organise (list anything you're running low on, make sure tins / packets that are first to go off are at the front, top up containers, straighten shelves and cupboards, do any little niggling maintenance tasks etc.). You may want to go back through the big organisational steps every year or so, but with regular cleaning and a mini monthly organise, you can likely maintain your beautifully functional kitchen for years. You will more than save that time back in terms of speedier meal prep.

Even if you don't manage to do this on a regular basis, you do now have both the knowledge and skills to bring your kitchen back into a place of calm efficiency whenever needed.

MAKING THE KITCHEN A MORE JOYFUL PLACE TO BE

As a bit of a reward for all that hard work, we can now start thinking about adding those last few lovely touches to help make your newly organised kitchen as joyful as it can possibly be.

Music and podcasts

I love to cook with music or a good podcast. I have both a radio and speaker in my kitchen, and find it helps to cue my mind into relaxing as I cook. This is most especially helpful when I'm feeling particularly tired and frazzled at the end of a long day. A good kitchen playlist or a few saved podcasts definitely help to pass the time enjoyably while peeling, chopping and stirring.

Lighting

Good lighting in the kitchen is essential. Decent ceiling lighting and clean, clear windows provide ambient light, while task lighting – particularly over the Golden Work Space – is really useful. You can buy cost-effective and self-adhesive light strips, and even battery-operated LED spots to help with this.

If you have a kitchen big enough to have a table in it, it is lovely to have directional or overhead light above the table for breakfasts and lunches, and then moodier lighting for intimate dinners – candles and lamps are essential for me.

Beauty

Of course, our kitchens need to work hard for us, but that doesn't mean we can't make them beautiful, too. Creating an appealing space reminds us that our time in the kitchen is as important and can be as joyful as time spent anywhere else in the house.

'Make the kitchen a place you want to be, and you'll want to be there more'

I love fresh flowers and plants in the kitchen, even just a bunch of fresh herbs in a jug of water or pots by the windowsill. I also like to have bowls of fruit, fresh eggs, tomatoes and other seasonal produce out on display. I keep my nicest hand soap and hand cream by the kitchen sink, as well as having a few candles to light as I cook. There's always a fresh, clean apron ready to use and I hang artwork and happy family photos on the wall. I even decorate my kitchen at Christmas and for special occasions.

It's these little, but important, moments of beauty that make my kitchen a more desirable place to be, even when I'm shattered. They're not expensive, and they don't require a re-design, but they (along with all the tips I've already shared for creating order and logic) make all the difference to how much I feel like cooking.

IN SUMMARY

1. The quality of our everyday diets, and therefore ultimately our health, depends on how well our kitchen is set up to support us in cooking nourishing meals from scratch. A well-organised and efficient kitchen can be, quite literally, life-changing.

2. Everything in the kitchen should be Useful, Used and Usable. Responsibly dispose of anything that isn't. Good organisation needs space to breathe, which can be achieved through an editing and decluttering process.

3. Try to give everything a specific place to live – have a logical system of organisation that is easy for everyone to maintain. Function in the kitchen needs to come before appearances.

4. Keep healthy food at eye level and make it as easy as possible to access. Keep less healthy food in opaque containers, above or below eye level, and make it harder or more inconvenient to access. This applies to store cupboards, shelves, worktops and fridges.

5. Try to keep a stock of wholesome storecupboard staples to hand, so you don't have to go shopping every time you are hungry.

PART TWO

Plan

PLAN YOUR MEALS

I hope that you're feeling a little more in control of your kitchen and that the very practical steps we've taken so far have built your confidence to move on to the next set of skills to becoming an Organised Cook. Let's start with meal planning.

MENU / MEAL PLANNING

Meal planning has been crucial in my work with clients for years. Having a rough idea of what we are going to cook and eat each day is powerfully helpful. It doesn't have to be elaborate or wildly original, but an outline of a plan, typed into our phones, scribbled on the back of an envelope, written on a black or whiteboard, or in a dedicated diary, will save time, money and effort. If you don't follow any of the other advice in this book, I urge you to at least give basic meal planning a go for a couple of weeks and see just how transformative it is.

While I understand that this might sound like a whole new level of organisation that you simply don't have time for, in fact, the busier and more overwhelming life gets, the *more* beneficial a rough meal plan. We know we're going to need to make these decisions every single day anyway, so why not lump them all together and get it done in 10 minutes once a week? I promise you, it will be a relief.

Before you say that you don't know what you're going to want to eat for lunch next Tuesday, for example, I will quickly counter with two reassurances. The first is that you don't have to stick to the plan. There are no prizes for the most perfectly followed meal plan. You can change your mind if you want to. And, secondly, chances are that there'll be more moments where it *is* helpful, than times when you want spontaneity. So, give it a go, and then judge for yourself.

> **TIP:** *Keep your old meal plans and their associated shopping lists in a small folder alongside your recipe books. Mark each one with the season and add any notes or comments about things that worked well, or that perhaps you'd do differently next time. That way, you'll have a personalised 'back catalogue' of seasonal plans you can fall back on if you don't have the time or inclination to make a new one each week.*

For anyone new to this, here's a step-by-step guide to meal planning. You can use this as a template to get you started, but soon enough I'm sure you'll develop your own system. There is no one 'right' way.

> **TIP:** *There is a plethora of meal planning apps and programmes available online, if this process is something you'd prefer to digitise. I generally do mine on paper, in the notes section on my phone, or on a magnetic meal planner that I have up on my fridge. But if you're more tech-minded, take a look on the app store.*

THE STEP-BY-STEP GUIDE

STEP 1: START WITH A STOCK CHECK

Look at any food you already have in the kitchen, especially in the fridge, that needs eating sooner rather than later. Check your fruit bowl, freezer and cupboards, too, so that nothing goes to waste.

Jot down any specific fresh produce that you will be getting this week. This is useful if you eat seasonally by getting a vegetable box delivery, you grow your own, or you are going to a local farmer's market or farm shop.

STEP 2: HIGHLIGHT YOUR BUSIEST DAYS

I do this by putting a star next to them on my meal planner. This means I'll either need very quick and easy dishes planned for that day, or to think about making enough beforehand for leftovers. It's obvious, but don't plan dishes that take a long time to prepare or cook on busy days.

And, conversely, if there are any meals you'll be eating out, you can cross those off!

STEP 3: ADD PROTEINS

Jot down a list of the various proteins available to you. Unless you are vegetarian or vegan, this will include meat, fish, eggs, natural yoghurt, pulses – beans, chickpeas, lentils, peas – as well as soy, nuts and seeds etc. In terms of good nutrition, I try to get a portion of protein at every meal, while varying the sources of protein across the week. Protein is important for helping us to feel full after a meal, for balancing blood sugars and for the growth and repair of our tissues. As it is so important, and often one of the more expensive ingredients to buy, it makes sense to plan meals around these protein sources.

Each week I try to cook five different protein foods. This might change a bit depending on the seasons and what is available but, as an example, it usually includes:

1. Chicken or turkey

2. Chickpeas / lentils / beans or other pulses

3. Eggs

4. White fish or shellfish

5. Oily fish

I don't tend to eat red meat on a weekly basis. This is both for health reasons (it is recommended that we don't eat too much processed meat, for example) and, importantly, for environmental reasons. Therefore, I don't usually plan it into my weekly menu. We do have it occasionally (there are just four recipes for red meat in this book), but it will be for a special occasion, and I always try to buy high-quality, ideally organic, regeneratively farmed and high welfare meat. This makes it expensive, which is another factor that limits how often I buy it.

If you are vegetarian or vegan, think about planning a variety of plant-based protein sources – for example:

1. Chickpeas

2. Black beans / kidney beans

3. Lentils

4. Nuts or nut butters

5. Tofu

6. Eggs / natural yoghurt / cheese (if vegetarian)

As you make your list of proteins, think about use-by dates and freshness. For example, I often shop on a Wednesday, so I will almost always have fresh fish on Thursdays, as this is quickest to spoil. Pulses and eggs can be included later, as they won't go off so fast. But make sure you look at the use-by dates when buying, and re-jig your plan (or safely freeze) accordingly, to avoid potentially expensive waste.

STEP 4: NOW START TO PULL EVERYTHING TOGETHER INTO COMPLETE DISHES

They don't have to be 'recipes' as such (unless you want them to be and, if so, make a note of which book the recipe is in and the page number or website). They could instead be as simple as lists of foods to assemble together, or rough notes to flesh out later.

Don't be afraid of planning leftovers as main meals (or call them 'planned overs' or 'meal prep' if you don't like the word leftovers). Jot down a few ideas of how to pep them up or re-imagine them for use the next day.

I try to include a handful of 'filler meals', which are those easy, adaptable, go-to ideas that can plug any gaps, such as soups, pasta dishes, quick curries / dahls, salads and frittatas. You'll find recipes for all of these super versatile dishes later in the book.

Here's an example of a weekly meal plan from my folder.

Wednesday *Shopping day*	Lunch: Red lentil pasta salad Dinner: Vegetable stir-fry with cashew nuts, coriander and lime
Thursday *White fish*	Lunch: Vegetable soup with seeds and oatcakes Dinner: Steamed white fish with greens, new potatoes and pesto dressing
Friday* *Oily fish*	Lunch: Leftover vegetable soup with feta and rye toast Dinner: Smoked mackerel salad with rocket, cucumber, tomatoes and pumpkin seeds.
Saturday *Pulses*	Lunch: Out with friends – meal not required Dinner: Vegetarian curry served with spinach
Sunday *Chicken*	Lunch: Roast chicken with roasted vegetables and steamed broccoli Dinner: Leftover curry, served with brown rice and fresh coriander / lime
Monday *Eggs*	Lunch: Leftover cold roast chicken with salad and tomatoes Dinner: Frittata with seasonal veg and feta
Tuesday*	Lunch: Leftover frittata and salad Dinner: Bottom-of-the-fridge vegetable stew (using up leftover vegetables before shopping day tomorrow), served with quinoa, lemon and lots of fresh herbs

You'll notice I don't plan breakfast as it's the one meal of the day when I tend to stick to just a few ideas on rotation. I don't often plan desserts either, as we generally have some fresh fruit, natural yoghurt or a couple squares of dark chocolate. However, you will find a few recipes for both breakfasts and desserts in this book, just in case you're after ideas to include in your plans.

I do, however, plan my lunches and, as I work from home, they tend to be leftovers to save time. I rarely eat out or make a packed lunch on a weekday at the moment, but I did in the past when I worked in an office. Leftovers make great packed lunches, providing there is a fridge to store them in and the ability to reheat them, if needed. There are lots of ideas in the recipe section (see pages 80–211).

STEP 5: MAKE A SHOPPING LIST

Finally, go through your plan and make a list of all the ingredients you'll need to buy, taking into consideration what you already have. You'll have made a list of what you have during your stock check, so look at this against your plan for the week and see what gaps there are.

MAKING NOURISHING MEALS

This book really isn't about *what* to eat, so much as *how* we plan, shop, organise and cook. However, I am also conscious that my expertise is in Nutritional Therapy, so I wanted to include a very short explanation of one simple tool we can use to help when planning a really nutritious and varied diet.

It covers six key categories or 'pillars' of food that are important for our overall nutrition and which I try to consider at every meal:

1. ½ plate of **vegetables** (equates to about 2–3 portions)

2. ¼ plate / palmful of **protein**

3. ¼ plate **minimally processed carbohydrate** (such as pasta, potatoes, rice, quinoa or good bread). This is optional and can be included if you have higher energy requirements or feel hungry.

4. A little **healthy fat** (such as a drizzle of olive oil to dress my vegetables, or a sprinkle of seeds to add some crunch)

5. A pop of **flavour** (healthy food absolutely needn't be boring, so I add some extra flavour – lemon zest, vinegar, black pepper, fresh herbs, chilli flakes, roasted garlic, tahini, fresh lime juice and tamari sauce are a few examples)

6. A piece of **fresh, seasonal fruit** for pudding

Remember that, if – or should I say when – this can't be achieved at every meal or on every day, that's OK. Enjoying just one or two of these food pillars at each meal is an achievement and something to feel proud of. We can work up from there over time.

If you'd like more information on exactly what to eat for a balanced and nutritious diet, see my book, *Nourish & Glow: The 10-day Plan*, which was entirely dedicated to the principles and practice of Positive Nutrition and dives into far more detail. You'll also find lots of free advice and healthy recipes on my website – www.ameliafreer.com.

STICKING TO YOUR PLAN

So, we've made ourselves a rough meal plan of nourishing dishes and created a shopping list with all the very best of intentions. Your fridge and store cupboard are stocked and ready to feed you healthily for the week, but then a tempting advert pops up on TV or social media and you end up ordering a delivery for dinner instead. Or perhaps a poster on your way to work persuades you that you really *do* deserve to buy and eat that chocolate treat.

These are examples of the power of food advertising. An entire industry dedicated to persuading us to buy and eat, when we weren't really planning to. This is unfortunate when it comes to sticking with a healthy diet, as the vast bulk of food advertising is for ultra-processed foods and drinks that are generally high in fats, sugars and salt. Wholefood producers simply don't have the budget to compete.

Many of us already understand that food is an emotional subject, intimately linked to our memories and feelings. Food marketing executives know and understand this, too. They use emotionally powerful language and images to persuade us that eating their food will bring us feelings of comfort, reward, generosity, nostalgia, belonging, vitality and a whole host of other positive feelings.

Here's a little tool that may help you disarm the power of food advertising in your life.

Think 'END' when you come across a food advert. It will help to steer you to become a more conscious observer and consumer.

E = Emotion: What EMOTION is this advert trying to produce?
See if you can spot and name the emotional tool the marketing department has tried to use to tempt you into buying. Is it comfort, reward, generosity (a particularly sneaky one, I think), nostalgia, power, personal pleasure, belonging, health, identity, adventure, vitality etc.?

N = Nutrition: Does this advert support or nourish my NUTRITION?
Would eating or drinking this product nourish our physical, emotional or social health? Or might it be detrimental in some way?

D = Display: Would it be so appealing if the food or drink in the advert wasn't so beautifully DISPLAYED?

Imagine the food plonked on a battered plate or the drink poured into an old plastic beaker. Would it draw us in as much if there had been less food styling, photo editing and tempting additions of ice beads or steam trails?

Once we start to recognise these tactics, it can be quite a fun game to look more objectively at any adverts that come our way and see if we can identify the emotion they are invoking. It helps us to become more mindful about whether it is effectively persuading us to believe in that emotion, too.

Of course, it is ultimately up to us as individuals to make our own choices and be independent. Sometimes we might well end up choosing to be influenced by a food advert – and that's fine. But doing so consciously vs unconsciously is very different. Sometimes it's OK to acknowledge that it's *just another food / drink* and move on with our day.

IN SUMMARY

1. Give meal planning a go. Having a rough idea of what you're going to cook and eat each day can save an enormous amount of time, effort, money and mental load. You don't have to stick to it rigidly, but simply having a plan can be a big relief in your busiest hours.

2. Start with a stock check. Highlight the busiest days. Add proteins. Jot down complete dishes. Plan-in leftovers. Plug gaps with quick-and-easy filler meals. And write a shopping list.

3. Keep all your old meal plans and shopping lists in a folder, so you've got a personalised back catalogue of ready-made, seasonal plans you can use time and again.

4. Remember that a nourishing meal can be created from almost any whole food ingredients by using this simple guide: ½ plate vegetables, ¼ plate of protein, ¼ plate of minimally processed carbohydrate (if needed), a little healthy fat, a pop of flavour and a piece of fruit for pudding.

5. See through the clever temptations of food advertising by using the 'END' tool.

PART THREE

Shop

HOW TO SHOP WELL

Eating well *always* begins with shopping well.

It may be true that we are what we eat, but what we eat begins with what we buy.

We simply cannot eat a healthy diet if we don't buy (or grow) healthy food. It's an often overlooked yet crucial part of enjoying a nourishing diet.

Importantly, shopping well for healthy food does not have to be wildly expensive, difficult or time-consuming. And eating well is absolutely not about superfood powders, obscure ancient grains or artisan vegan snacks. For me, it's about choosing simple, whole food ingredients and learning how to combine them to make hearty dishes. Over the next two sections of this book, including all the recipes, I hope to share lots of ways to do exactly that.

Shopping well seems so simple on the surface, yet it probably isn't something we were ever actually taught how to do. By that I mean shopping well for ourselves, for the planet and for our wallets. But while food shopping may not be something *we* have given much thought to, I can promise you that retailers most certainly have.

'There can be no inspired cooking without inspired shopping and, behind that, inspired farming.' Michael Pollan

The competition for our grocery spending is fierce, so all sorts of tactics are deployed to entice us to spend more of our hard-earned money. It's important to say that I don't think these merchandising 'tricks' are malicious, they're just business strategies in a highly competitive market. But understanding them can help us as individuals, as we can then know how to avoid them and make our food shopping as nourishing and cost-effective as it can possibly be.

Here are some tactics that I have found to be really helpful:

1. DON'T GO SHOPPING HUNGRY OR THIRSTY

I don't think it's necessarily true that we buy more food if we shop hungry (although of course this is possible), but from personal experience, I find that I am more likely to reach for convenient snacks or pre-prepared food when I do. Things that I could potentially eat one-handed on the way home, that will give me the quick burst of energy that I'm craving. In my experience, hunger makes it much harder to stick to a planned shopping list of whole food ingredients.

Plan to go shopping after a meal or have a nourishing snack (ideally which includes some source of protein, such as some nuts) and a glass of water half an hour before you head out. Don't forget that we sometimes interpret thirst as hunger, so having some water is a good idea.

2. TASTE MINT

My friend and fellow Nutritional Therapist, Nicola Moore, talks about three types of hunger:

Head hunger: When we see or smell something that makes us want to eat a certain food. It is a hunger driven from imagination and sensory inputs, rather than from our body actually needing energy. This is how a lot of food advertising works, and the hunger is specific to the food we are imagining or seeing.

Mouth hunger: A desire to experience specific tastes. This could be driven by emotional cravings, boredom eating, or simply habit, but the hunger we experience is directed towards a very specific food or category of food tastes (salty, sweet, alcohol etc.), and wouldn't be satisfied by any other foods.

Stomach hunger: A rumbling, growling stomach and real physiological need for energy and food. This is 'true' hunger – our body telling us to eat to nourish and fuel ourselves. Eating anything would alleviate this hunger, including a big salad.

It's important to become mindful of which hunger we might be experiencing, as it allows us to start to recognise that some types of perceived hunger might just be thoughts, rather than physical signs that our body needs us to eat. Brushing our teeth or sucking on a sugar-free mint can be a helpful way of reducing mouth hunger and, to a certain extent, head hunger. We generally don't want to mix the lingering minty flavour with other tastes, as we know from experience it isn't always an enjoyable or pleasant sensation.

TIP: *Keep two large boxes or baskets in the car boot for use when shopping. Rather than using bags or packing your shopping in store, unload everything into these baskets straight from the trolley when you get back to your car (one for store-cupboard staples and one for fridge / freezer). It will make unloading and unpacking at home so much faster.*

SUPERMARKET SHOPPING AND MERCHANDISING

Merchandising is the art of staging a store to encourage us to buy more high-profit foods (often processed ones) and, reportedly, it really works. Supermarkets spend millions of pounds every year on it. If we want to shop consciously, however, and serve our *own* best interests, it can be helpful to understand what some of these strategies might be, so that we can avoid being swayed.

1. FRESH PRODUCE IS MOST OFTEN NEAR THE ENTRANCE TO THE STORE

This is, apparently, to encourage us to feel like we are entering a 'natural' and colourful space. Filling our trolleys with fresh produce first also helps us to feel we have 'done' the healthy thing already – and may then be more likely to buy treats and snacks later on.

However, we can flip this on its head and use it to our health advantage. We tend to put more into our basket or trolley at the start of our shop, so we can begin by aiming to fill approximately half our trolley or basket with a rainbow of colourful fruits and vegetables. Keep in mind that just because we've got off to a great start, doesn't mean we don't need to keep on track in the rest of the store.

2. ITEMS PLACED AT EYE LEVEL ARE IN THE PRIME SELLING SPACE

It's where we spend the greatest amount of time looking, so it makes sense for shops to place things with the highest profit margins there: best-sellers, impulse purchases, ultra-processed foods, and more expensive variants of popular products. So, you need to look beyond eye level. The top shelves tend to hold specialty products and premium brands, but the lower shelves are where the bargains, bulk products, less processed and discounted offers are most often found – so look down. A disproportionately large amount of the cost of basic foods is spent on marketing when buying branded products. Unbranded or own-brand versions tend to be very similar in quality (and nutrition), but much better value for money. This is particularly true for whole food ingredients.

Perhaps more worryingly, items specifically placed at kids' eye level may be done so in the hope that children will persuade their parents to buy them. This is harnessing 'pester power' and is something many parents dread when shopping with children (myself included). There's not much we can do to stop children seeing items at their eye level, and shopping without children isn't an option for many. There are a few strategies you could use while shopping to help prevent children becoming overwhelmed or upset. You could ask them to write or draw a short list of items that they will be in charge of adding to the trolley – and you can give them some controlled choice as you go around the shop, such as 'shall we get red apples or green?' Also try to avoid the aisles you know are the most tempting to them!

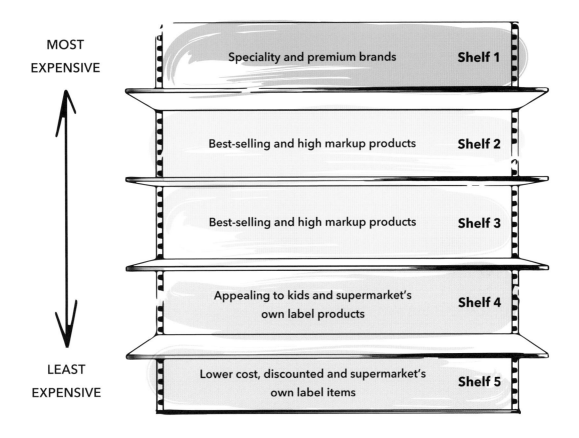

MOST
EXPENSIVE

Speciality and premium brands	**Shelf 1**
Best-selling and high markup products	**Shelf 2**
Best-selling and high markup products	**Shelf 3**
Appealing to kids and supermarket's own label products	**Shelf 4**
Lower cost, discounted and supermarket's own label items	**Shelf 5**

LEAST
EXPENSIVE

3. STAPLES, LIKE BREAD, EGGS AND MILK ARE USUALLY PLACED IN THE FURTHEST CORNER OF THE STORE

This means we walk all the way through the shop and pass a large number of additional products to get to them. If possible, try going around the outside of the supermarket, rather than through the aisles, to reach these staples. This will significantly reduce the amount of ultra-processed foods you have to pass before reaching them, and therefore hopefully reduce temptations along the way.

4. CHECKOUT TEMPTATIONS

The checkout area (including the aisle ends) is often designed for impulse purchases, something that is more likely to happen if we are kept waiting in line. It builds on the idea of rewarding ourselves for a task completed (the weekly shop, in this case).

Although many shops are now committed to a healthy checkout, and bravo to that, the end of the aisles next to the checkouts are often still packed with brightly packaged, ultra-processed convenience foods.

We can start by being conscious of this strategy and set ourselves the goal of not adding anything to our basket or trolley once we join the checkout queue. It might also be helpful to choose the checkout aisle with the fewest temptations around it — often this is the self-checkout area.

5. SEASONAL DISPLAYS

Valentine's Day, Easter, summer, Halloween, Christmas etc. are big marketing opportunities, and often find the shops packed with sweets, alcohol and snack foods with a big 'treat yourself' vibe. These are often placed right at the entrance to the store and are almost always highly colourful and enticing. While there is absolutely nothing wrong with embracing each holiday and special occasion wholeheartedly, it's sensible to take a moment to think about what we really need and want to eat and buy before being drawn in by the display. It can be helpful to try to do our whole planned shop first, before coming back to browse these displays. We're less likely to overbuy if we've already filled our basket or trolley with nourishing foods.

6. A WORD ABOUT LOYALTY CARDS

Loyalty cards and programmes offer retailers a goldmine of information about our shopping habits and can be highly effective ways to keep us shopping at the same stores. Think carefully before accepting a loyalty card and be aware of exactly what's in it for us. Be conscious that we may save significantly more money by shopping around, rather than staying loyal to one store and accruing points.

TIP: There are a wonderful array of independent food shops and markets offering a wide choice of ingredients and produce. Some of these options can work out significantly cheaper and / or be more environmentally friendly than shopping at the major supermarket chains. This is especially true when it comes to specialty items, organic fruit and vegetables, higher welfare meat and fish, or bulk-buy items. The key, I think, is to shop around, keep your eyes open, and ask friends and family for local recommendations. And don't be afraid of trying out a new way of shopping once in a while.

A HEALTHY APPROACH TO ONLINE SHOPPING

We've covered lots of ways to shop well in person at the supermarkets, but many of us (myself included) are choosing to shop more online. So how can we ensure that our digital shop is as healthy and nourishing as it possibly can be?

1. FILL HALF YOUR VIRTUAL BASKET WITH FRESH PRODUCE

Some research suggests that we buy fewer fruits and vegetables when shopping online, as we are concerned that they might arrive bruised, overripe or damaged. But we also know that eating lots of fruits and vegetables is fundamental to a healthy diet.

So, if this is a concern, consider signing up to a weekly fruit and vegetable delivery box or seeking out your local greengrocer or market. Don't forget to browse the online frozen fruits and vegetables, though – many of which are just as nutritious as their fresh alternatives but there isn't the risk of bruised or spoiled produce.

Aim to start your online grocery shop by adding fresh or frozen fruits and vegetables to your basket, just as you would if shopping in store. As it's hard to know what half the volume of your trolley would look like virtually, perhaps aim for a minimum of 6–8 different vegetables, and 3–5 different fruits as a guide, and try to vary these according to the seasons (see page 63 for a guide to what's in season when).

2. DON'T OVERLOOK THE NUTRITION INFORMATION

We are reportedly more likely to check out the nutrition information labels when shopping in-person than we are to click into these facts online. Perhaps take a moment next time you shop online to look at the nutrition information for any processed or packaged foods you regularly add to your basket – you might be surprised to see what a supposedly 'healthy' product actually contains. (See pages 58–62 for more information on how to read nutrition labels.)

3. BE WARY OF ONLINE MARKETING TACTICS

When you buy something from an online grocery shop it may be added to a digital 'favourites' list even if, as far as you're concerned, it is a one-off purchase. It can then be offered back to us repeatedly through targeted advertising. This is often done as a prompt when we've finished our shopping as something we might have 'forgotten'. Such prompts can end up turning our one-off treat into a once-a-week habit, subtly encouraging us to over-purchase and over-consume. Sponsored items may also be slipped into our favourites list, in the hope that we might add these to our baskets. So, generally, I suggest you ignore these steps and skip quickly on through to the checkout.

4. STICK TO YOUR SHOPPING LIST

It's good to think about what you need to buy before sitting down to place your online order and try to stick strictly to this list. It's just as important to do this when shopping online as it is when shopping in person, as buying only what you need ultimately helps to minimise food waste and saves us money. Something else that helps to make this is easier is to avoid online shopping when you're feeling hungry, exhausted (or have had a couple of glasses of wine!).

UNDERSTANDING FOOD LABELLING

If there is one aspect of healthy food shopping that I think confuses people more than anything else, it is understanding what food labels and nutrition information really mean. So, if this is something that leaves you feeling overwhelmed, then please know you are not alone. There's quite a lot to it, and often not much explanation given. Hopefully, I can address some of that confusion here.

The basics

- In the UK, nutrition labelling is compulsory for pre-packaged foods but is not always necessary in full for whole foods (such as fruits and vegetables) or those sold loose. I find this reassuring and therefore try to buy mostly things that don't need a label in the first place.

- Certain pieces of information must be included on food packaging by law, including the name of the product, the weight or volume, the ingredients listed in order of volume or weight – so it will always start with the largest ingredient and end with the smallest, and allergy information, alongside preparation or storage instructions, details of the manufacturer, date marks etc. (although there are some exceptions).

- There is also mandatory back or side-of-pack nutrition labelling, giving values of energy (in kilojoules and kcal), total fat, saturated fat, carbohydrates, sugars, protein and salt per 100g or 100ml. Many also include values of these nutrients per portion.

- Front-of-pack nutrition labelling, including the traffic light system, is currently voluntary.

UNDERSTANDING USE-BY, BEST BEFORE AND SELL-BY DATES

Use-by dates are the most important dates to consider. Food should not be consumed after the use-by date, as it could potentially put our health at risk. It's important to store the food according to the packaging instructions for this date to be valid (i.e. keep it in a fridge at the correct temperature, if that is what's required). If we don't follow storage instructions correctly, the food may spoil sooner than the use-by date, and we could be at risk of food poisoning.

Freezing food from fresh can extend its life beyond the use-by date, but it's important to freeze it as soon as possible after purchase and to follow any instructions on the pack when cooking or defrosting it. Use-by dates on pre-frozen foods, however, should always be followed.

Best before dates are more about quality than safety. When the date has passed, it doesn't necessarily mean that the food will be dangerous or put us at risk of food poisoning, it might just not taste so great. Again, this date is only accurate if we store the food according to the packet instructions (such as 'store in a cool, dry place' or 'keep in the fridge once opened'). It's usually OK to eat foods after the best before date if they look, smell and feel all right. Use your judgement.

Sell by dates are not required by law and are primarily instructions for shop staff, rather than for consumers. Look out for use-by and best before dates instead.

DECIPHERING NUTRITION INFORMATION

WHAT DOES THE TRAFFIC LIGHT SYSTEM REALLY TELL US?

The traffic light system on food packaging was designed to help us see at a glance if the food we are buying has high (red), medium (amber) or low (green) amounts of total fat, saturated fat, sugars and salt per portion.

It is usually displayed alongside the percentage of our Reference Intake (RI) for the day (which tell us how much a portion of that food contributes to the total fat, energy, sugars and salt an average adult doing an average amount of activity 'should' eat each day).

Generally speaking, it's sensible to eat a diet that is lower in saturated fat, sugars and salt. So, more greens on the traffic light system is considered better than more ambers or reds.

I think this colour coding can potentially be helpful, but the traffic light system is not everything when it comes to making healthy choices.

For example, it only really applies to packaged foods. Ideally, I'd encourage you to aim for a mostly whole foods diet – which doesn't use a traffic light system at all, since most of the ingredients would be unpackaged. Secondly, it doesn't tell us anything about how processed a food is, or what its micronutrient (vitamin and mineral) content is. Finally, it doesn't take into consideration seasonality, sustainability, or the wider context of our individual diets. So, while it is absolutely helpful to be able to make informed choices when it comes to our food shopping and nutrition, I'd suggest that the traffic light colours are just one piece of the puzzle.

WHAT ARE ULTRA-PROCESSED FOODS (UPFs)?

Rather than looking simply at the traffic light system, I want to encourage you all to look at the degree of processing your foods undergo when trying to decide which ones to buy.

Of course, some processing of food is helpful and necessary, prolonging shelf life perhaps, or making foods more digestible or palatable. Cooking itself is a form of processing. The nutritional issue here is not, therefore, with *processed* foods. It is with *ultra-processed* foods.

Ultra-processed foods are not just modified or merely processed foods (like ingredients made into recipes, or whole foods packaged to prolong their shelf life). They are industrial formulations manufactured from substances extracted from foods, and typically include additives to enhance their appearance and taste. They are specifically designed (usually in a lab) to be extremely palatable, long-lasting and convenient, and are typically high in sugar, unhealthy fats and salt, but low in fibre, protein, vitamins and minerals.

'Reducing ultra-processed foods in our diets is probably one of the most important things we can do to improve our nutrition'

They are also extremely common, and often cleverly marketed, using colourful packaging, health claims, special deals with retailers, vast advertising campaigns (including to children) and ingenious use of print and online media. They are often highly profitable, as each stage of the processing and branding journey adds value. Something that a humble apple or bag of spinach can't really compete with.

> **TIP:** *Remember, ultra-processed foods are not designed with our health in mind. They are instead designed to make us into profitable customers, by being ultra-palatable, cleverly advertised and encouraging us to over-consume.*

This group of foods is something I am increasingly conscious of, and keen to spread the message about, as a growing body of evidence suggests that ultra-processed foods are potentially harmful to health, especially when eaten regularly and in large quantities. On the flip side, research has also suggested that decreasing the amount of ultra-processed foods we eat may substantially improve how nutritious our diet is, which may then have a knock-on benefit to our wider health.

However, it is important to add that all foods, even ultra-processed ones or those with mostly red traffic light labels, can have their place within a balanced diet in moderation (if we want them). But whole foods tend to have significantly more nutritional value (fibre, protein, micronutrients, phytonutrients etc.) per unit of energy than their highly processed alternatives. They offer us a lot more nutritional bang for our buck. So that is what I am focusing on in this book, and what all the recipes I've shared here are based upon.

HOW TO SPOT ULTRA-PROCESSED FOODS

Food manufacturers are *not obliged to label when something is ultra-processed*, so it can be hard to identify them without knowing what to look for.

Generally speaking, the most practical way to identify if something is ultra-processed is to read its list of ingredients.

1. Are there items on the list that you wouldn't find or have in your own kitchen? Can you recognise all the ingredients?

2. Is the list of ingredients very long? Be conscious that it may well be an ultra-processed food if there are five or more ingredients.

3. Does it have a surprisingly long shelf life?

4. Is it being aggressively marketed and branded? You're unlikely to see a TV ad for apples or broccoli!

Here are a few things to look out for on labels, which indicate that a food may be ultra-processed:

- Isolated proteins: hydrolysed proteins, soya protein isolate, gluten, casein, whey protein, 'mechanically separated meat'

- Processed sugars: fructose, high-fructose corn syrup, 'fruit juice concentrate', invert sugar, maltodextrin, dextrose, lactose

- Hydrogenated or interesterified oils

- Cosmetic additives: gelling / glazing agents

- Emulsifiers: soya lecithin, mono- and diglycerides, polysorbates, carrageenan, guar gum

- Sweeteners: aspartame, cyclamate, stevia, saccharin, sucralose, xylitol, sorbitol

- Thickeners / bulking agents

- Flavours

- Preservatives

Examples of ultra-processed foods:

Packaged snacks, industrially produced bread or bread products, certain breakfast cereals, biscuits, ice creams, chocolates and confectionery, pastries, carbonated and energy drinks, canned / packaged / dehydrated soups, sauces, desserts or drink mixes, sweetened and flavoured yoghurts, processed or flavoured dairy drinks (including chocolate milk), margarines and spreads, meal replacement shakes, pastries, cakes, processed meats (burgers, nuggets, hot dogs etc.) and some pre-packaged ready meals. (There are some ready meals that are not ultra-processed, so it's a case of reading the ingredients labels and ascertaining whether it contains the same ingredients you would use if you were cooking it at home).

Examples of whole foods or minimally processed foods:

Vegetables and fruits (including frozen), wholegrains (such as rice, oats and other cereals), eggs, beans and other legumes, dried fruits, nuts and seeds, fresh and dried herbs, fresh, chilled or frozen unprocessed meat or fish, milk, yoghurt without additives, tea, coffee, water, unrefined oils (such as olive oil), maple syrup, honey, butter, cheese, sea salt, cane sugar, minimally processed breads (made with just flour, yeast, water and salt), fermented alcoholic drinks without additives.

HOW TO READ THE NUTRITION INFORMATION

We've checked out the traffic light system on the front of the packet, and worked out if it's ultra-processed or not from the ingredients list, now it's time to take a look at the back of the packet and scan the nutrition panel. This is where we'll find lots more information on what's contained inside, and the potential effect the food might have on our nutrition and, ultimately, our health.

It can be helpful to start by taking a look at the portion size given. Does it look realistic to you? The best way to know this for sure is to weigh or measure out a recommended portion size and then you'll know whether this is in line with what you usually serve yourself or family. This is particularly worthwhile doing with breakfast cereals or items we buy regularly, as the recommended portions are often significantly smaller than we might realistically serve.

Now look at the following four areas of the nutrition information panel, to give you a good overview of its overall nutritional value:

- **Is it low in sugar?** <5g per 100g. Be conscious, however, that values given for sugars don't tell you whether they are naturally occurring sugars (i.e. from fruits) or added sugars. Look at the ingredients list for sugar, honey, syrups, nectar, molasses, fruit juice concentrate or anything ending in –ose (such as fructose, glucose, maltose, dextrose etc.). If it's in the ingredients list, it's an added sugar, however natural it might sound.

- **Is it low in saturated fat?** <1.5g per 100g

- **Is it high in fibre?** >6g fibre per 100g (I like to see >10g per 100g) If you're choosing between two products and they are otherwise very similar, I'd suggest opting for the one with more fibre. Many of us need to consume more fibre, and should be aiming for 30g a day.

- **Is it high in protein?** >15g protein per 100g Technically, this would mean that at least 20% of the energy value of the food comes from protein but, in reality, I look out for products that have more than 15g protein per 100g.

A NOTE ON CALORIE COUNTS…

You might notice that I haven't mentioned calories. While it is absolutely true that managing your energy intake is important in terms of weight management, I don't find that calories are enough of a complete or accurate representation of the energy balance overall to be worth focusing too much time on. Why? Because calories alone don't tell us anything about the other nutrients in a food, whether it will satisfy and nourish us or leave us craving more, whether it's ultra-processed, or whether it's a whole food. Nor does it begin to take into consideration our individual digestion, absorption and metabolism. So, while I know that many people interpret a low-calorie count as a proxy marker for something being 'healthy', I want to encourage us to think a bit more broadly than that. Remember: good nutrition is not just about calorie maths.

HEALTHY-EATING TIP: *If you don't have time to scrutinise all your shopping like this (most of us don't), then pick just one or two packaged foods to look at each week. Might there be a more nutritious alternative available? And if you're not sure which part of the nutrition information matters most, I'd suggest trying to prioritise reducing ultra-processed foods in the first instance.*

SHOPPING WELL FOR LESS

For most of us, a significant portion of monthly outgoings is spent on groceries, and that spend looks only set to rise. Trying to balance the competing demands of making sure our budget stretches to cover all the necessary items on our shopping list, while also optimising nutrition, satisfying different tastes or food intolerances, and being mindful of sustainability and single-use plastic is hard. I really get it. And I understand how tiring and stressful it can feel to find that balance week-in, week-out.

So, how can we keep a rein on food costs, without compromising too much on our nutrition, sustainable habits or health? Many of the key tried-and-tested ways to shop well for less have

The illustration above shows when fruits and vegetables are in season. While I try to eat fruit and veg that is local as well as seasonal, this isn't always possible and can sometimes be expensive. I wanted to provide a guide that might help you to ascertain when to buy so that you get the best seasonal produce that, even if it's not grown locally, will still be flavourful and nutritious.

been covered in detail in the previous pages of this book, but perhaps not always in the context of budget. If combined, however, they can certainly add up to significant savings.

To start with, it can be helpful to make a note of your food spending from the past 1–2 months. Include everything from main shops, top-up shops, takeaways, coffees and meals out. Then you'll know where you're starting from and where you could potentially make adjustments. Remember, your food spending is not just in the supermarket.

Take a look at the following ideas and suggestions and see if there are any that may be relevant to your food spending habits. Try picking one idea each week to focus on, and see how much of an impact you can make by implementing the change over the course of a month or so.

1. **Meal planning** helps us buy only what we need, makes the most of the ingredients we do buy and reduces the risk of waste (see pages 40–7). Write a meal plan for one week and see how much of a difference it makes.

2. **Reuse and re-imagine leftovers** to minimise food waste (wasted food = wasted money). Try to go a week without throwing any edible food away.

3. **Write a shopping list** and try to stick to it rigidly. Even a couple of impulse purchases each shopping trip can really add up over a month or year (see the shopping advice on pages 50–62).

4. **Buy in bulk** where possible and decant into containers (see pages 26–7). Consider splitting a bulk order with a friend or neighbour to reduce the risk of food waste if this is helpful.

5. **Shop around** to find the best deals (which may be beyond the supermarkets). The discount supermarkets offer fantastic ranges of whole foods, including some organic produce, and are consistently significantly cheaper than other supermarkets. And on that note, please don't worry if your budget doesn't stretch to buying everything organically. It is far more important to eat a balanced diet, filled with varied whole foods, fruits and vegetables, than it is to restrict your diet because you're worried it's not organic. Just wash ingredients well and peel them, if necessary.

6. **Take a quick photo of the inside of the fridge and store cupboard before every big shop** (aka the 'shelfie'). This can help to prevent us from inadvertently doubling up on anything, which reduces the risk of one of those items going off before we get around to using it.

7. **Avoid or reduce discretionary food and drink spending** (snacks, coffees, bottled drinks, meals out etc.). This can add up to a surprisingly large amount.

8. **Shop seasonally**, as what's in season is more abundant, and the laws of supply and demand mean that costs generally go down as supply goes up.

9. **Be inventive** with the less expensive foods, such as pulses, whole grains, potatoes, eggs, natural yoghurt, seeds, and seasonal fruits and vegetables. Frozen and minimally processed tinned or jarred produce is often just as nutritious as fresh, but significantly cheaper (and reduces the risk of accidental food waste). Here are some of the ingredients I turn to most often to keep tabs on my shopping budget.

   - Bananas, apples / pears / oranges, lemons and frozen fruit / berries tend to offer the best value for money when it comes to fruit. Look out for special deals and seasonal varieties beyond these basics (especially 'wonky' produce).

   - Potatoes, sweet potatoes, carrots and squash are all very filling and highly nutritious, and are often a good price as they store so well (especially in the autumn and early winter).

   - The price of green vegetables (broccoli, beans, kale, cabbages, courgettes, salads, fresh herbs etc.) will vary hugely according to seasonality, so it pays to know what's in season. A simple shortcut is to look at the country of origin – if it's been grown in Britain, it usually means it's in season (or has been appropriately cold stored). Try to avoid expensively air-freighted produce, and don't forget to look in the freezer section for frozen greens, too. Frozen peas, spinach, sweetcorn, baby broad beans and green beans are great nutritious options.

   - Tomatoes are usually cheapest when jarred or tinned (and may even offer some nutritional benefits when processed like this), although the price of fresh tomatoes tends to fall in the summer as their European season peaks.

   - Onions and garlic tend to be relatively cheap, and can keep well in a cool, well-ventilated place, so it pays to buy them in bulk. They can also be frozen – just peel, chop and freeze on trays, then scrape them into a bag when frozen solid (this stops them forming a big clump).

10. **Avoid pre-prepared foods** as these almost always cost a premium. You're essentially paying for someone else's time alongside the ingredients. Hopefully the strategies you've already learnt in this book will help you find enough time to prepare your own meals from scratch instead.

11. **Cook and eat at home** as much as possible – including making packed lunches and packed snacks.

12. **Swap one thing per shop for a cheaper alternative**. If you're used to buying certain premium or branded items, try swapping one item each shop for a cheaper alternative and see if you notice a difference. Often, the price difference is far more a reflection of marketing costs than it is of ingredient quality or nutritional value.

13. **Buy higher quality meat and fish in smaller quantities.** As a little tip, the smaller the meat is chopped, the further it goes and the less it costs. You can make a small amount of meat

or fish go a long way if you are creative with how you cook it. Organic, high-quality mince is almost always better value than a steak (and a small amount can be bulked with green or Puy lentils and chopped vegetables to make it stretch a lot further).

- Check out the Marine Stewardship Council website to see whether the fish you are planning to buy is a sustainable option, or whether there are better choices to make. From a nutrition perspective, we don't really need to eat fish more than twice a week (one portion of oily fish, one of white fish or shellfish). Tinned fish, especially mackerel and sardines, is often very cost effective, as is frozen fish.

- Look out for local farmers and see if you can buy direct. This can be more economical than buying from farm shops, for example. Even better if you can find and support those farmers practising regenerative agriculture – using grazing animals to help rebuild soil fertility and health – who are providing a crucial lifeline to the future fertility of our farmland.

TIP: *Keep all your sustainable and plastic-waste-reducing shopping kit (cloth produce bags, reusable shopping bags, lidded refill containers, glass jars etc.) all together in one grab-bag and try to put everything back into the car / main shopping bag at the end of each trip, so you don't have to find it every time you want to leave the house, or end up having to buy new bags every shopping trip.*

IN SUMMARY

1. Don't shop hungry or thirsty, but do try tasting mint before going to the supermarket.

2. Be aware of the various merchandising tricks that supermarkets use to tempt us (and our children) into buying more. Plan your supermarket shopping trip to avoid falling for them. Try shopping beyond the supermarket, if you'd like to reduce your exposure to these strategies.

3. If shopping online, try to fill half your virtual basket with fruits and vegetables (or buy them elsewhere). Don't forget to check out the nutritional info, be wary of online marketing tactics, and try to stick to your shopping list.

4. When reading nutrition labels, scan the traffic light system, read the ingredients list (to help spot ultra-processed foods), and check the nutrition information panel to see if it is low in sugar and saturated fat, and high in fibre and protein.

5. There are lots of ways that this book can help support you to shop well for less. From meal planning to leftovers, and reducing food waste to being inventive with cheaper ingredients. Try one or two ideas at a time to see what impact they could have on your grocery spending.

PART FOUR

Cook and Clear

HOW TO BE A BETTER COOK

TIPS FOR MORE EFFICIENT COOKING AND CLEARING

Along with getting our kitchens and cupboards arranged into efficient order, which obviously helps to avoid time spent searching for ingredients or a piece of kit, there are plenty of practical tips I've picked up over the years (often when working alongside professional chefs on my books or workshops) to help make the cooking experience more efficient. Think of each one as a little pro boost, helping to make our home cooking that bit slicker.

If following a recipe, read it right through to the end before starting. That way, you'll know where you're heading and can decide if any steps could be completed concurrently (and also if any steps or ingredients could be skipped or simplified).

Prepare all the ingredients before starting to cook. This might not suit everyone, but it suits me. I like to get all the ingredients I need onto my worktop, and then complete the bulk of my preparation before starting to cook – unwrapping, washing, peeling, chopping etc. That way, I don't end up burning something while my back is turned chopping. Also, while you're preparing the vegetables for one meal, you may as well prepare them for the next. Just as it's a great idea to batch cook the main course or dish, we can also batch prepare vegetables, too. I love eating lots of vegetables (2–3 portions per meal), but I don't love preparing them, so I'm definitely a fan of strategies to speed things up.

Smaller pieces = faster cooking. I know this is an obvious tip, but the smaller the pieces of food are, whether that be vegetables, meat, fish, potatoes or similar, the less time they take to cook. Chop, grate, blend or slice things smaller, and the meal will be ready quicker. If you're not fast at chopping, then I'd recommend watching some knife skills videos (there are plenty freely available on YouTube) or enrolling on a course at a local cookery school. So few of us have actually been taught how to chop efficiently and safely, yet it makes a huge difference to how confident we feel in the kitchen. It might also be worth investing in a mandoline or food processor. The grater setting on a food processor is brilliant for super-quick, big batches of coleslaw or other grated salads, and you can also use the blade and pulse setting to make a quick vegetable flavour base for cooked dishes with onion, celery, carrots and garlic. Make sure your knives are sharp – a blunt knife is both dangerous and a time-waster.

Use the cooking time. If a dish takes a while on the hob or in the oven, make the most of this time by getting ahead with a few things for the next day – preparing vegetables or side dishes, tidying up the kitchen or laying the table. This means that when the meal is finished, it's just the last bits and pieces of washing up to be done and everything else is already sorted.

Pre-heat the oven and pans. This needn't be for hours, but we can give our food a head-start by putting it into an already-hot oven or saucepan. I usually allow about 5 minutes to get the oven up to temperature, and up to a minute on the hob for my saucepans (especially if they are heavy ones). Any more than this can be a waste of energy. Also, use saucepan lids when bringing food up to boil or keeping it simmering – they make a big difference.

Line oven trays. It makes clearing up so much quicker. I buy compostable parchment paper for this – you can buy them as pre-cut sheets for ultimate time-saving. I don't use aluminium foil, both from a sustainability perspective and due to concerns around possible leaching of the aluminium into the food.

Pack the oven. If we've bothered to turn the oven on and are cooking a dish already, we may as well make the most of that time and energy (and therefore cost), by adding another couple of items that don't need much prep. Things like a tray of vegetables to roast, a few jacket or sweet potatoes or some cloves of garlic in olive oil to make a confit, tend to be my go-to extras. Then we've got leftovers ready for another meal with no further cooking required.

Delegate. Decide ahead of time if someone else in the house could safely be in charge of certain meals each week, and then let them get on with it. They might not do it exactly as we would, but hovering about and making 'suggestions' is often just as much work as doing it ourselves. So, try to delegate the task and then let go. Be in another room if that helps (bonus marks if you put your feet up!). I am a big believer in the importance of encouraging older children and teenagers to be self-sufficient in the kitchen. Cooking is a crucial life skill and needs to be practised. Obviously supervise if sharp / hot things are involved, but perhaps start by choosing meals that they *can* safely prepare for themselves and work up from there.

Don't be afraid to 'split shift' cooking. It's totally fine to break down cooking into chunks of time and split them across the day. Perhaps we have 20 minutes in the morning or over lunch that could be spent prepping all the ingredients for later, or 10 minutes to clear the work surfaces and lay out the equipment we'll need before heading off to work. This is how all professional kitchens operate, and we can use the same principles at home. Use whatever time you have for cooking wisely – it doesn't have to be done all at once in the evening. Also, if you have a slow cooker, it's the perfect piece of equipment to use if you generally find you have more time or energy earlier in the day.

Soak don't scrub. I know that it's lovely to wake up to a spotless kitchen without any washing up but, for the sake of time, I'll often leave dishes to soak overnight in hot soapy water. In the morning it then takes just a couple of minutes to wash up, rather than spending ages scrubbing when I'm already tired. It's also worth getting any dirty pans straight into water once you're done with them, as dried-on food is a real pain to clean. You could keep a big bowl filled in the sink while cooking for exactly this purpose. More on cleaning tips and tricks on pages 76-7.

ALMOST-INSTANT VEGETABLE IDEAS

I eat a lot of vegetables and encourage my clients to do the same. I try to have six portions of different veg a day, which works out at 2–3 portions per meal (yes, even at breakfast). They're sources of fibre, vitamins, minerals and beneficial phytonutrients but are relatively low in energy density. They are fundamentally important to building a healthy, balanced diet. Plus, I genuinely enjoy eating them, and love how much more energetic and nourished my body feels when I eat lots. But, I know that preparing lots of veg can be time-consuming. As a result, I don't make specific vegetable dishes or recipes much of the time – often it is just a very quick, almost-instant side instead.

Here are some of the options I fall back on. If cooking *is* required, I most often bung them in the steamer for a few minutes until just tender, drizzle with olive oil and a squeeze of lemon juice, and I'm done.

- Pre-washed salad / rocket / watercress / spinach / lettuce

- Cherry tomatoes

- Sliced cucumber

- Sliced bell peppers

- Pre-cooked beetroot

- Carrot sticks or grated carrot

- Tinned or frozen sweetcorn

- Frozen peas / green beans / broad beans / edamame beans

- Tenderstem broccoli / fresh green beans / mange tout / sugar snap peas / asparagus – I find these the quickest cooked vegetables to prep (and you can buy them ready-trimmed)

- Steamed broccoli / cauliflower (fresh or frozen)

- Frozen spinach for soups, stews, casseroles etc. or fresh baby leaf spinach for salads or smoothies

- Pre-prepared stir-fry vegetable packs (these are great way to get masses of vegetables into a single meal)

- Tinned tomatoes – no prep required and I use them in lots of my cooking

MAKING THE MOST OF BARGAINS, GLUTS AND EXCESS PRODUCE

Preserving through fermentation, drying, curing, freezing or canning has been practised for many hundreds of years, and was an essential lifeline in the times before widespread food security and refrigerated supply chains.

I wanted to mention it here as it is a skill and practice that has fallen a little by the wayside, yet can absolutely still offer us modern cooks some benefits. Not to mention the satisfaction that comes from stocking up our cupboards or freezers with nourishing food for a future date and reducing food waste. It's particularly helpful if we grow our own (or have generous friends who do), or if we come across a fantastic deal on produce that might be slightly going over or is perfectly in season and therefore abundant.

I am not a fermentation or canning specialist, though, so I will leave those topics in the safe hands of the experts (there are plenty of books available on each of these subjects if you search online). I am, however, good at batch cooking and freezing. Freezing is such an easy way to store batch-cooked food, but I'm conscious that not everyone has a huge amount of freezer space, so just freeze what you can. Batch-cooked portions can usually be kept safely in the fridge for three days (see page 35 for more information on safely storing leftovers and cooked food).

Here are a few suggestions on how to use certain ingredients when you have more than you need:

1. **Fresh herbs / spinach / rocket or other tender greens:** These can be whizzed into a quick salsa verde (see page 195) as it is so useful to have in the freezer. It is so satisfying to transform a huge pile of slightly wilted leaves into something zingy and delicious to use on pasta or as a sauce for meat or fish. I freeze it in large silicone ice-cube trays or in old jam jars. Or you can finely chop a mixture of herbs and freeze them in ice-cube trays with olive oil. These can be popped straight into a pan the next time you are cooking some vegetables.

2. **Tropical fruit, such as mango or pineapple:** Peel, core and blend the flesh into a purée, then freeze it. This works well as a yoghurt topping or to pep up a fruit salad or smoothie. You could also blend the purée with a little yoghurt and freeze directly into lolly moulds.

3. **Summer berries / foraged blackberries:** Freeze these in a single layer on a large tray, and then decant them into a large reusable bag (they all clump together if you don't freeze them flat first). You can add a handful of them to overnight oats, smoothies, into crumbles or puddings, or warm them through from frozen in a saucepan with the juice of an orange for a quick compote.

4. **Apples, pears and other stoned fruit:** Core and peel, then stew with a little cinnamon – no need to add sugar – and blend. Freeze in portions as a compote. The same treatment is used for pears (and a mixture of the two is delicious). I'll also turn plums, greengages or other stoned fruits into a compote in much the same way (I remove their stones first).

5. **Bananas** (especially slightly overripe ones): Peel, roughly chop and freeze. You can then blend the banana flesh directly from frozen with a tablespoon of almond or peanut butter for the most delicious, creamy and nutritious 'ice cream' dessert. Or add them to smoothies or use to make banana bread.

6. **Tomatoes / courgettes / peppers / aubergines:** These just cry out to be made into an unctuous ratatouille, which can then be frozen in portions.

7. **Fish:** Extra portions of cooked or uncooked fish can be pulsed in a food processor or blender with herbs and a little mashed potato, rolled into balls and frozen, for quick fish cakes or fish fingers. Just ensure the fish wasn't frozen beforehand (it's not advised to freeze foods more than once).

8. **Cauliflower, chillies, onions, carrots or cucumber:** These are so simple to turn into pickles (see my basic recipe on page 196). Quick pickles are such a treat to liven up salads, soups and stews.

9. **Wine:** Leftover wine (yes, really!) can be frozen into silicone ice-cube trays or small containers, and then popped out to use in cooking whenever required.

10. **Eggs:** If you have leftover egg whites from baking, but don't want to cook with them straight away, you can freeze them (though not the yolks). Just pop the whites into a silicone tray, freeze until solid, then pop out into a clip-top container. Wash the tray well afterwards.

HEALTHY-EATING TIP: *I make a stock pretty much every time I cook a chicken. It ekes every last bit of nutrition and goodness from the bird and stretches how many meals I can get from one chicken. I just take the meat off the carcass and add all the bones, skin etc. into a large saucepan alongside a halved onion, carrot, celery and some herbs. Cover with cold water and simmer for 2–3 hours (keeping an eye on it to make sure it doesn't boil dry), or put in a slow cooker and cook overnight. Strain through a sieve and discard the bones. Re-boil the stock with the lid off until it has reduced to about a quarter of its original volume. You can then pour the concentrated stock into silicone ice-cube trays and pop one out any time you need a homemade stock cube in soups, stews, curries etc.*

KITCHEN CLEANING TIPS AND TRICKS

This might not be the most exciting section of the book, but keeping the kitchen clean and tidy is important for food hygiene. It also makes cooking a meal more enjoyable if we don't have to clear the drying rack, do all the washing up or unload the dishwasher and wipe the surfaces beforehand.

I actually enjoy cleaning and making my kitchen a lovely place to be. I tend to tidy up as I go along. As we spend so much time in our kitchen, mess does tend to accumulate, so I try and keep on top of it. 'Everything has its place' is my motto! I know that other people like to do it all in one go, so do what works best for you.

Here are a few tips and tricks on how to clean various items in the kitchen, which will help to keep it a clean and cheery place, without the use of expensive and harsh chemicals.

Microwave: Fill a ceramic, microwave-safe bowl with cold water and add half a lemon. Microwave on full power for a few minutes. The steam and lemon will loosen grime and cut through grease. All you need to do then, is wipe it down with a damp sponge and your microwave will be gleaming.

Work surfaces: I use a natural multi-surface cleaner that I get in re-fill pouches. But a trusty mixture you could try making at home is: 1:10 parts pure castile soap (a vegetable soap made from olive oil) to water, decanted into an old spray bottle, with 10 drops of tea tree oil added (for its scent and disinfectant properties). Spritz onto work surfaces after cooking, and wipe clean with a damp sponge. It also works well on hobs, splashbacks and tiles.

Sink: Bicarbonate of soda works wonders on stainless-steel sinks. Just scatter it around and rub in with a damp microfibre cloth before rinsing thoroughly with hot water. If you have limescale build-up around your kitchen taps, pour some white vinegar onto a kitchen towel until it is soaking wet, then wrap it around the affected area (you can use a rubber band or something to secure it in place, if necessary). Let it sit for 1–3 hours before scrubbing with a brush and rinsing thoroughly. Avoid the vinegar getting onto worktops, as it could damage or discolour them.

Fridge: It's easiest to deep clean the fridge when it's pretty empty. Start by getting everything out and onto the table or work surface (keeping things in cool bags if necessary). Remove all the shelves, including those from the fridge door, and wash them in hot, soapy water – washing up liquid works best, I find. Dry and polish any glass with a clean tea towel. Then wipe the shelf brackets, seals, floor and sides. Avoid using harsh disinfectants or cleaning sprays directly in the fridge, though, as they can contaminate or taint the food – stick with just a sponge or microfibre cloth and a bowl of water with a drop of washing up liquid, or use a castile soap spray. Check that the drain hole at the back is clean and clear. If you've got time, it's a good opportunity to have a thorough fridge re-organisation (see pages 28–35).

Dishwasher: Completely empty the dishwasher and remove the drawers (if possible). Wipe around the seals and edges with hot, soapy water and a sponge (this is surprisingly gross and deeply satisfying). Remove, empty and clean the filter in more hot, soapy water. Rinse well before replacing. Add 2 cups of white vinegar to the bottom of the dishwasher before running an empty cycle on the hottest setting.

MY KITCHEN CLEANING CHECKLIST

This is the checklist that I generally try to follow. Obviously, how often you need (or want) to clean your own kitchen will be different and will depend on many different factors. But this works pretty well for me as someone who cooks every day and has a young child and all the mess that comes along with that. I definitely recommend getting a good podcast or some music on while doing this!

DAILY

- Put away any food – from shopping, meals, leftovers etc.

- Dispose of any food waste and packaging responsibly into the compost, council food waste, recycling or dustbin.

- Load / unload the dishwasher (if you have one).

- Wipe down all surfaces, including the table and hob.

- Wash up and put everything away. Did you know there is an order to washing up that helps make it as efficient and effective as possible? Fill the sink or a washing up bowl with plenty of hot soapy water (this saves water, compared to doing it under a running tap), then wash everything in the following order, rinsing under hot water once cleaned to remove all traces of washing up liquid. Doing it in this order means that greasy pans don't leave stubborn streaks on glasses:

  1. Glasses

  2. Cups

  3. Cutlery

  4. Plates

  5. Kitchen equipment

  6. Pots and pans

- Quickly clear out and rinse the sink.

- Sweep or vacuum the floor, if necessary

- Tidy away stray items that have ended up in the kitchen or on the table – everything from handbags and post, to toys and telephones.

HEALTHY-EATING TIP: *A handy little trick I share with clients is that once the evening meal is tidied and put away, we then 'shut' the kitchen. Turn off the lights, music and any other devices, perhaps even shut the door and spend time in another room. This can create a visual and psychological message that eating time is over, helping us to avoid mindless late-night grazing, drinking or snacking.*

WEEKLY

- Wipe down the fridge.

- Wipe down exteriors of appliances and bins.

- Spot clean cupboard / drawer fronts, if necessary.

- Wash the kitchen floor.

- Wash dishcloths, aprons and tea towels.

- Empty and rinse the dishwasher filter, if you have one.

MONTHLY

- Deep clean the fridge.

- Deep clean the dishwasher, if you have one.

EVERY 2–3 MONTHS

- Deep clean the oven (or set it to self-clean, if there is a pyrolytic function).

- Clean out drawers and cupboards, including the drawer dividers (which are a bit of a magnet for crumbs).

- Wipe down any open shelves and containers.

EVERY 6 MONTHS +

- Defrost and clean / organise the freezer.

- Go through the kitchen organisation process outlined in the ORGANISE chapter.

IN SUMMARY

1. Take a look at the tips for more efficient cooking and clearing on pages 69-70 There are lots of helpful ideas to bring an efficient professional boost to your everyday home cooking.

2. Eating lots of vegetables (I recommend aiming for six portions a day) is a fundamental part of building a healthy, balanced diet. But that also means lots of vegetable prep. However, not all vegetable sides need to be elaborate or specific recipes. Take a look at the list of almost-instant ideas on page 71 for lots of everyday inspiration.

3. The freezer, if you have one, can be a really brilliant tool to make the most of seasonal produce bargains, gluts and leftovers (see pages 74-5).

4. Keeping the kitchen clean and tidy is important for food hygiene reasons, but also to make cooking a far more enjoyable and efficient experience. See the cleaning tricks and checklist on pages 76-9.

The recipes in this section are all about real-life healthy eating

They are made predominantly from whole foods, all cooked from scratch and created with both taste and nutrition in mind. But, crucially, they are also a toolkit of ideas to help you put all the strategies from the first half of this book into action.

Here, you'll find recipes that lend themselves to batch cooking, freezing and preparing ahead. Recipes that can be infinitely adapted to suit what is in season and what you have to hand. Recipes that make the most of your well-stocked kitchen cupboards and fridge, so you can rustle up something nourishing in next-to-no time. Recipes that truly feed mind and body.

But I want to encourage you to interpret them loosely. Most of these dishes don't need every ingredient in order to work well and can handle a great deal of switching and changing while still tasting great.

There's a lovely analogy to being a musician to be made here. If your kitchen is now a finely tuned instrument, these recipes are the musical score. And the meals you make? They are, of course, the music. Just as a musician is free to interpret music in whichever way they like, you are free to interpret these recipes. Liven them up, play them down, adapt them to suit your tastes and mood, and make them your own.

Most of all, I hope you enjoy cooking and eating them.

A note on prep and cook times. For me, prep time indicates the work you do before you actually start to cook: gathering, weighing, chopping, peeling etc. Cook time is how much time this dish will take you to cook from start to finish, once the prep is out of the way. I hope you'll find this guide useful when doing your meal planning.

GF: *Gluten-free*
DF: *Dairy-free*
KIDS: *Particularly suitable for children*

Where any of the above appear in brackets, this indicates that ingredients can be substituted easily to make the dish gluten- or dairy-free, vegetarian or vegan.

RECIPES

Seedy Cinnamon Bircher Base

This recipe is a go-to in our household: a quick, one-bowl wonder packed with fibre, protein and healthy fats, helping to keep us energised, full and ready to take on the day. You can prepare the base mix in a batch ahead of time, then just scoop out a cupful or two as required, soaking it overnight to enjoy as Bircher, serving with some cold milk as muesli, or warming through for a comforting winter porridge. A winning solution for any busy household.

VEGAN / (GF) / DF / KIDS
Serves 6
Prep time: 6 mins

160g oats (use gluten-free,
 if necessary)
65g Brazil nuts, roughly chopped
6 tbsp raisins (about 80g), or
 8 dates, roughly chopped
2 tsp chia seeds
2 tbsp sunflower seeds
2 tbsp pumpkin seeds
2 tbsp ground flaxseeds
2 tsp ground cinnamon
pinch/good grating of nutmeg
 (optional)

Mix all the ingredients together and store in an airtight container until needed.

For Bircher (makes 1 serving) – Mix 60g of the base mix with roughly a cupful (230ml) of milk of choice and leave to soak overnight in fridge. Serve as is, or add a little more milk, or some yoghurt and fresh fruit. Keeps for 2–3 days in the fridge once soaked.

For muesli – Add milk of choice and enjoy, perhaps with some fresh fruit if you fancy.

For porridge (makes 1 serving) – Mix 60g of the base mix with roughly a cupful (230ml) of milk of choice or water in a small saucepan. Place the pan over a medium heat and bring to the boil, then reduce the heat and simmer gently for 5–10 minutes until the porridge is your desired consistency, adding a little extra splash of milk if needed. Serve as it comes, or with a spoonful of fruit compote or some sliced fresh fruit on top.

Tip: *If you can't eat nuts, leave them out and add more seeds. Feel free to mix up the type of nuts or seeds used. I have also made this with dried figs or dried apple – both delicious alternatives.*

Lemon and Poppy Seed Granola

This zesty, crunchy granola absolutely deserves to become a regular fixture at your breakfast table. It's filled with nourishing ingredients and a batch stays fresh for a month, so it's well worth the minimal prep for the joy it brings to a month of mornings. If you want more of a lemony hit for an extra-zesty start to your day, use lemon juice instead of water.

VEGAN / (GF) / DF / KIDS
**Serves 6-8 as a main breakfast or
   12-14 as a topping**
Prep time: 15 mins
Cook time: 45-50 mins

2 tbsp coconut oil or mild /
   light olive oil
2 tbsp maple syrup or honey
zest of 2 lemons
2 tbsp poppy seeds
1 tbsp sesame seeds
1 tbsp flaxseeds
2 tbsp pumpkin seeds
2 tbsp sunflower seeds
200g oats (use gluten-free,
   if necessary)
pinch of sea salt
100g whole blanched almonds
   (or other nuts of choice),
   roughly chopped
2 tbsp water or fresh lemon juice

Preheat the oven to 150°C fan/170°C/gas 3 and line a baking tray with parchment paper.

Place the coconut oil with the maple syrup or honey and the lemon zest in a small saucepan over a low heat and stir until melted. Pour into a large mixing bowl. If using olive oil, you can skip this step and instead place the olive oil, lemon zest and maple syrup or honey straight into a large mixing bowl.

Add the seeds, oats, salt and almonds to the oil mixture and stir until everything is well coated. Finally, stir in the water or lemon juice.

Pour onto the prepared baking tray and bake at the bottom of the oven for about 45-50 minutes, stirring every 10-15 minutes until everything is golden and starting to crisp.

Remove from the oven and allow to cool completely.

Store in an airtight container for up to 4 weeks.

TIP: *If you don't have all the seeds individually, use 6 tablespoons of mixed seeds and 2 tablespoons of poppy seeds instead. Scale up the quantities if you want to make a bigger batch.*

Banana, Blueberry and Oat Triangles

On busy days, a good breakfast can help set us up for the day. These nourishing, fruity, oaty triangles can be made in advance and kept in the freezer for the days when we need them most. They don't take long to defrost (although you could always pull one out the night before if you know it's going to be an especially busy morning). Simply knowing that there's something ready to grab and go helps me feel calmer amongst the inevitable morning chaos.

(VEGAN) / (GF) / DF / KIDS
Makes 8 triangles
Prep time: 8 mins
Cook time: 30 mins

100g porridge oats (use gluten-free, if necessary)
1 ripe banana, mashed
20g chia seeds
20g sunflower seeds
40g ground almonds
125ml boiling water
1 tbsp maple syrup or honey
60g blueberries
pinch of salt

Preheat the oven to 180°C fan/200°C/gas 6 and line a small square baking tray (about 20cm) with parchment paper.

In a large mixing bowl, mix all the ingredients together.

Spread the mixture out into the prepared tray and bake for 25–30 minutes, or until the top is starting to brown.

Remove from the oven and allow to cool before slicing into 8 triangles.

Store in an airtight container and freeze for up to 3 months.

TIP: *In autumn and winter, try swapping the blueberries for frozen berries, blackberries, or grated apple and a pinch of cinnamon. Double the quantities, if you want a bigger batch.*

Breakfast Muffins

A muffin and a nice cup of tea can be a glorious start to the day. These nourishing muffins contain 'hidden' vegetables, alongside nuts and seeds, helping to boost our fibre intake, as well as providing a good dose of other essential nutrients. They are a great snack for hungry kids, too.

VEGETARIAN / (GF) / DF / KIDS
Makes 12
Prep time: 20 mins
Cook time: 25–30 mins

2 ripe bananas, peeled and mashed
200g courgettes, coarsely grated
200g carrots, coarsely grated
2 large free-range eggs
120ml oil (I use light olive oil)
100g coconut sugar (or sugar
   of choice)
40g raisins
40g walnuts, chopped
2 tbsp ground flaxseeds
pinch of sea salt
200g self-raising flour (use gluten-
   free, if necessary)
1 tsp baking powder (use gluten-free,
   if necessary)
20g sunflower seeds

Preheat the oven to 160°C fan/180°C/gas 4 and line a 12-hole muffin tin with muffin cases.

In a large mixing bowl, combine the banana, courgette, carrots, eggs, oil, sugar, raisins, walnuts, ground flaxseeds and salt. Mix well.

Stir in the flour and baking powder until just combined.

Spoon into the cases and sprinkle the sunflower seeds over the top. Bake for 25–30 minutes until golden brown on top and a skewer inserted into the centre comes out clean.

Allow to cool a little before eating, as they can come out of the oven quite gooey.

Store in an airtight container in the fridge for 3 days, or freeze them for up to 3 months.

TIP: *You can use any chopped nuts or seeds instead of walnuts.*

Seasonal Frittatas

Frittatas are a quick and easy way to get lots of vegetables into a meal while delivering on protein too. Almost anything goes when it comes to combinations and ingredients, so they're brilliant for using up leftovers, lonely veggies or last bits of cheese. As the frittata mixture cooks relatively quickly, if you want to add squash, pumpkin or roots (carrots, beets, potatoes etc.), steam or roast them first to sweeten and soften them a bit. Softer vegetables, like courgettes, peppers or tomatoes and any greens, can be grated or chopped before adding them raw to cook with the eggs. I like to keep things seasonal, if possible, so here are four variations that celebrate what's growing at any particular time of year. These are lovely served alongside My Favourite Green Salad (see page 117).
Each frittata serves 4 VEGETARIAN / GF / (DF) / KIDS

Spring – Asparagus, Pea and Broad Bean with Goat's Cheese

Light, bright and full of the joys of spring; the zingy goat's cheese adds a beautifully creamy finish that I love, though feel free to omit it (or swap for some smoked salmon) if you'd prefer.

Prep time: 5-10 mins
Cook time: 20-25 mins

1 tbsp olive oil
2 spring onions, trimmed and thinly sliced
1 bunch asparagus, trimmed and cut into 2cm lengths
150g frozen peas
150g frozen broad beans
6 large free-range eggs, whisked
50g goat's cheese, crumbled (optional)
small handful of whole picked mint leaves
½ red chilli, finely sliced

Heat the olive oil in a 24cm ovenproof frying pan over a medium heat and add the spring onions and asparagus. Fry gently for 2-3 minutes.

Add the peas and broad beans and a splash of water and continue to fry/steam for a further 3-5 minutes, until the peas and beans have just defrosted and the water has evaporated.

Preheat the grill to medium.

Season the whisked eggs and pour over the vegetables in the pan. Cook undisturbed for 5 minutes.

Scatter over the crumbled goat's cheese and place the pan under the grill for 5-10 minutes until golden brown and the eggs are set.

Scatter over the mint leaves and sliced chilli to serve.

Summer – Harissa, Roast Aubergine and Pepper

Smoky, luxurious and sweet, these Moroccan flavours married with vegetables from the Mediterranean are perfect for light summer lunches or packed up for picnics. You could roast twice the quantity of vegetables and toss the leftovers with quinoa, parsley and lemon juice for a quick salad.

Prep time: 10-20 mins
Cook time: 50-55 mins

1 small aubergine, chopped into
   2cm chunks
1 small red onion, thickly sliced
1 red pepper, deseeded and
   chopped into 2cm chunks
1 tbsp olive oil
1 tbsp harissa paste
6 large free-range eggs, whisked
40g feta, crumbled (optional)

Toss the aubergine, onion and red pepper in the olive oil and harissa so everything is evenly coated, then season with salt and pepper. Place in an even layer on a roasting tray and roast in the oven for 30-40 minutes until cooked through and starting to brown.

Preheat the grill to medium. Place a 24cm ovenproof frying pan over a medium heat and add the roasted vegetables. Season the whisked eggs and pour over the vegetables. Cook undisturbed for 5 minutes on the hob.

Scatter over the crumbled feta and place the pan under the grill for a further 5-10 minutes until golden brown and the eggs are set.

Autumn – Feta Beetroot, Sage and Pumpkin

Bright colours and rich flavours reflect the bounty of the autumnal harvest. This is both hearty and heart-warming, with a lovely bite to it. You could use the leftover butternut squash half to make the Chickpea, Butternut and Coconut Soup on page 98.

Prep time: 15 mins
Cook time: 50-55 mins

1 medium beetroot, peeled and
   chopped into 2cm chunks
½ small butternut squash, peeled
   and chopped into roughly 2cm
   chunks
2 tbsp olive oil
a few sage leaves, thinly sliced
6 large free-range eggs, whisked
40g feta, crumbled (optional)

Place the beetroot and butternut squash in an even layer on a roasting tray and drizzle over 1 tablespoon of the oil. Roast in the oven for 30-40 minutes until softened.

Heat the remaining oil in a 24cm ovenproof frying pan over a medium heat and fry the sage leaves for a few seconds before adding the roasted vegetables.

Season the whisked eggs with salt and pepper and pour over the vegetables in the pan. Reduce the heat and cook undisturbed for 5 minutes.

Scatter over the crumbled feta and place under the grill for 5-10 minutes, until golden brown and the eggs are set.

Winter — Potato, Kale and Cheddar

When the nights are long and cold, we need comfort food. What could be cosier than potato and cheese with a big helping of nourishing, wintery kale? I love this for a blustery Sunday night supper and enjoy any leftovers for breakfast on busy Monday mornings.

Prep time: 10 mins
Cook time: 25–35 mins

1 small onion, sliced
1 clove garlic, sliced
2 medium potatoes, chopped into
   1cm cubes
3 tbsp olive oil
2 large handfuls of kale, destemmed
   and chopped (or spinach /
   Swiss chard)
6 large free-range eggs, whisked
pinch of grated nutmeg
40g Cheddar, grated (optional)

Preheat the grill to medium.

Place the onion, garlic, potatoes and 2 tablespoons of the olive oil in a 24cm ovenproof frying pan over a low-medium heat. Sauté for 10–15 minutes until the onions are browning and potatoes are softening, stirring regularly so they don't burn.

Add the kale and the remaining oil and continue to cook for about 5 minutes, stirring occasionally, until the kale has wilted.

Season the whisked eggs with nutmeg, salt and pepper and pour onto the potato mixture in the pan. Reduce the heat to low and cook undisturbed for 5 minutes.

Sprinkle over the grated Cheddar and place the pan under the grill for 5–10 minutes until golden brown and the eggs are set.

NOTE: You can omit or substitute the Cheddar for any other cheese you like or have to hand. It would make a lovely, light festive meal with leftover blue cheese, I think.

TIP: *Frittatas are great for make-ahead breakfasts, packed and speedy lunches, or light suppers. Their versatility means they tend to be one of the go-to 'filler' meals on my rough weekly meal plan (see page 44).*

Turkish Eggs

My friend Katie first told me about this Turkish breakfast. She kindly made it for me one chilly Sunday morning and it has been one of my favourites ever since. It's inspired by menemen, *which is Turkish scrambled eggs cooked in a spiced green pepper and tomato sauce. Don't be put off if it all looks a bit mish-mashed — it'll still be delicious (and if you adorn it with lots of chopped fresh parsley and dill, it'll look pretty too).*

VEGETARIAN / GF / (DF)
Serves 2
Prep time: 5-10 mins
Cook time: 25-30 mins

1 small onion, finely diced
1 red or green pepper, deseeded
   and finely diced
1 tbsp olive oil
½ × 400g tin of chopped tomatoes
   or 200g cherry tomatoes
1 tsp red wine vinegar
pinch of mild red pepper or chilli
   flakes (Aleppo chilli flakes are
   lovely if you can find them)
4 free-range eggs, whisked
40g feta, crumbled (optional)
small handful of fresh parsley and dill
   (optional), roughly chopped

Place the onion, pepper and olive oil in a pan over a medium heat and fry for 10 minutes, stirring occasionally, until softened and starting to caramelise.

Add the tomatoes, vinegar, a pinch of salt and pepper and the chilli flakes, and leave to bubble for 5-10 minutes until the sauce has thickened slightly. (If using cherry tomatoes, it will take slightly longer for the tomatoes to break down and turn into the sauce.)

When the sauce has thickened and is bubbling all over, quickly stir in the eggs and cook for 2-4 minutes, stirring gently, until the eggs have cooked to your preferred consistency. Serve immediately with the feta and herbs sprinkled over the top, if using.

Persian Herb Frittata

I love using different fresh herbs and spices to make simple meals filled with flavour and as many greens as possible. So it's little wonder that this dish is a firm favourite of mine. Inspired by the Persian recipe kuku sabzi, *a wonderfully herby omelette traditionally served at Persian New Year, this abridged version cuts down on the ingredients list while making use of any leftover herbs in the fridge and adding feta for a salty hit. It works for any meal.*

VEGETARIAN / GF / (DF)
Serves 4
Prep time: 5 mins
Cook time: 15 mins

6 free-range eggs
large handful of mixed fresh green
   herbs (I used parsley, dill and
   coriander)
½ onion, diced
2 tbsp olive oil
50g feta, crumbled (optional)
Pomegranate seeds, to serve
   (optional)

Place the eggs and herbs in a blender and blitz until the herbs look very finely chopped.

Preheat the grill to high.

Place the onion and olive oil in an ovenproof frying pan over a medium heat and sauté for 8 minutes until soft and golden.

Pour the herb and egg mixture over the onion and cook for 2 minutes, keeping the pan moving by gently swirling and shaking it to stop the egg from sticking too much.

Crumble over the feta and place the pan under the grill for 2 minutes until golden brown and the eggs are set.

TIP: *This is a great way of using a glut of fresh herbs, or any mixture of them you have left over. You could bulk the herbs out with some spinach or rocket, if necessary.*

Chickpea, Butternut and Coconut Soup

This comforting soup is so easy to make that it's well worth doubling up portions to freeze for a rushed day. It makes the sort of bowl where you feel nurtured with each spoonful. The herbs and spices bring a depth of flavour to the gentle butternut, coconut and chickpeas, while a squeeze of lime and scattering of coriander lifts the flavours. You can blend it, but I love it chunky. A dollop of natural or dairy-free yoghurt also goes nicely.

VEGAN / GF / DF / KIDS
Serves 2–3
Prep time: 15 mins
Cook time: 45 mins

2 shallots or 1 small onion, diced
1 tbsp olive oil
2 cloves garlic, crushed
1 thumb-sized piece of fresh root
   ginger, peeled and grated
1 tbsp dried curry leaves (or 1 tsp
   mild curry powder)
1 tsp ground cumin
1 tsp ground turmeric
1 tsp ground coriander
large pinch of chilli flakes
½ small butternut squash, peeled
   and chopped into 2cm cubes
1 × 400ml tin of coconut milk
150ml vegetable stock
1 × 400g tin of chickpeas, drained
   and rinsed
1 lime, cut into wedges
small handful of fresh coriander
   leaves, to serve

Place the shallots or onion and olive oil in a pan over a medium heat and fry gently for about 10 minutes until softened. Stir in the garlic, grated ginger, curry leaves (or powder), cumin, turmeric, coriander and chilli flakes and fry for another 3 minutes. Add the butternut squash and fry for a further 2 minutes, stirring to coat the squash in all the spices.

Pour in the coconut milk and vegetable stock, cover with a lid and allow to simmer for about 20 minutes, or until the squash is soft.

Add the chickpeas and simmer uncovered for a further 10 minutes. Use the back of a wooden spoon or a potato masher to gently squash some of the butternut and chickpeas. Season with salt and pepper.

Serve with a squeeze of lime juice and some fresh coriander leaves.

TIP: *You can press unpeeled garlic cloves directly through a garlic press. Squeeze firmly and the flesh comes through the holes while the skin is left behind in the press. Simple!*

Miso Chicken Soup

This is a very popular soup in our family — deeply nourishing as well as being a great way to use up leftover roast chicken. It's very versatile — you could stir in some torn greens, like spinach, pak choi or kale, alongside the shredded chicken to up your vegetable intake. Or, for a more filling option, you could add some pre-soaked rice noodles.

GF / DF
Serves 2
Prep time: 10 mins
Cook time: 25 mins

2 tbsp olive or sesame oil
2 shallots or 1 medium onion, finely diced
1 punnet of mushrooms (about 200g), sliced
1 thumb-size piece of fresh root ginger, peeled and grated
2 tbsp sweet miso
1 tbsp tamari or soy sauce (use tamari if gluten-free)
600ml chicken stock or water
150–200g cooked chicken, shredded
juice of 1 lime
2 spring onions, trimmed and sliced
1 chilli, sliced
small handful of coriander, chopped

Heat 1 tablespoon of the oil in a pan over a medium heat. Add the shallot or onion and cook gently for 4-5 minutes, stirring occasionally.

Add the sliced mushrooms along with the remaining oil and fry for another 10 minutes until the mushrooms start to caramelise, stirring every so often.

Stir in the ginger, miso, tamari or soy sauce and stock and bring up to the boil. Reduce the heat and simmer for 5 minutes.

Add the shredded chicken and simmer for a further 5 minutes.

Season with salt and pepper and stir in the lime juice, sliced spring onion, chilli and coriander leaves to serve.

TIP: *If you want to batch cook and freeze portions of this soup, do so before adding the lime juice, spring onion, chilli and coriander leaves. It also makes a thoughtful and nurturing gift for friends who are feeling under the weather.*

Instant Roasted Pepper and Lentil Soup

This soup tastes like it's been an intense labour of love to make, but the reality is quite the opposite. It is as easy as blending a few store-cupboard ingredients together, then heating it through. I try to have a jar or two of roasted peppers to hand because they are so versatile and useful, as well as pre-cooked lentils – they deliver instant nourishment without any fuss. I like to serve this soup with parsley and some feta crumbled over the top, but that's totally optional.

VEGETARIAN / (VEGAN) / GF / (DF)
Serves 2–3
Prep time: 5 mins
Cook time: 5 mins

150g roasted peppers from a jar,
    drained
300g cooked brown lentils from a tin,
    jar or packet, drained if necessary
1 × 400g tin of chopped tomatoes
½ tsp smoked hot paprika
200ml vegetable stock
1 tsp red wine vinegar
small handful of fresh parsley,
    roughly chopped
20g feta, crumbled to serve
    (optional)

Place the drained peppers, lentils, tomatoes, paprika, vegetable stock and vinegar in a blender and blitz until very smooth.

Pour into a saucepan over a medium heat and heat gently. When just simmering, take off the heat and season with salt and pepper to taste.

Serve with some chopped parsley and crumbled feta, if you like.

Tip: *Try this topped with a drizzle of tahini and some toasted seeds for a nourishing vegan alternative.*

Instant Spinach, White Bean and Lemon Soup

This ticks all the boxes for those busier-than-busy days. A simple soup for when you've only got a few minutes between commitments but want to eat something good. It won't set the culinary world alight, but it's incredibly quick, filling and nutritious, so I had to share it here. This is a book about making the most of our time in the kitchen, after all! If you'd like an extra kick, sprinkle with some chilli flakes. If you have any left over, it can be frozen, too.

VEGAN / GF / DF
Serves 4
Prep time: 5-10 mins
Cook time: 5-10 mins

240g baby leaf spinach
3 tbsp extra-virgin olive oil
2 x 400g tins of cooked white beans, drained and rinsed
600ml vegetable stock
juice of 1 lemon
chilli flakes, to serve (optional)

Wilt the spinach in a saucepan with 1 tablespoon of the olive oil over a medium heat.

Put the wilted spinach, beans and stock in a blender and blitz until very smooth. Depending on the size of your blender, you might need to do this in a couple of batches.

Pour the soup back into the saucepan and heat gently to just simmering, stirring occasionally.

Take off the heat and stir in the remaining olive oil, the lemon juice and season with salt and pepper. Scatter with some chilli flakes, if you like, and serve immediately.

TIP: *If you have some cavolo nero pesto in the fridge (see page 192), or a good shop-bought version, add a dollop on top of the soup.*

Kale, Potato and Pecorino Soup

A twist on the classic leek and potato soup. You can blitz this if you prefer a smoother soup but I love it chunky and hearty so that it feels almost vegetable-stew-like. The grating of pecorino or Parmesan really deepens the flavour. Waxy potato varieties (which hold their shape when cooked) include Jersey Royals, Charlotte and Maris Peer.

VEGETARIAN / (VEGAN) / GF / (DF)
Serves 4
Prep time: 10 mins
Cook time: 30 mins

1 carrot, peeled and roughly chopped
1 leek, trimmed and roughly chopped
8 mushrooms, roughly chopped
2 tbsp olive oil
1 clove garlic, thinly sliced
pinch of dried mixed herbs
4 medium waxy potatoes, peeled and
    cut into 1–2 cm cubes
pinch of chilli flakes
900ml vegetable (or chicken) stock
200g kale, stems removed and leaves
    roughly chopped
zest and juice of ½ lemon
pecorino or Parmesan, grated to serve
    (optional)

Place the carrot, leek, mushrooms and olive oil in a large saucepan and sauté over a medium heat for about 10 minutes until starting to caramelise. Stir every so often so it doesn't burn.

Add the garlic, herbs, potatoes and chilli flakes and sauté for a further 2–3 minutes, stirring occasionally.

Pour in the vegetable stock and bring up to the boil. Reduce the heat and simmer for about 8 minutes until the potatoes are almost cooked through. Stir in the kale leaves and cook for a further 2–3 minutes.

Take the soup off the heat, add the lemon zest and juice and season with salt and pepper. Blitz in a blender or serve as it comes with some grated pecorino sprinkled over the top, if you like.

TIP: *If you have any pecorino or Parmesan rinds lurking in the fridge, add these to the soup while it is simmering and they'll add an extra umami boost. Make sure you remember to remove them before blending or serving.*

Baked Caponata

This is a low-maintenance traybake which just requires quick chopping and roasting to produce. It works as a side dish with a piece of baked white fish, chicken or grilled halloumi, but it's also lovely blended into a quick pasta sauce (which is often a great a hit with the little ones), or into a soup with a little vegetable stock. It's even great on toast with an egg for breakfast. This will keep in the fridge for 3-4 days.

VEGAN / GF /DF / KIDS
Serves 2 as a main or 4 as a side
Prep time: 10 mins
Cook time: 1 hr

1 aubergine, chopped into 2.5cm pieces
1 courgette, chopped into 2.5cm pieces
1 red pepper, deseeded and chopped into 2.5cm pieces
1 red onion, peeled and thickly sliced
1 stick of celery, cut into 1cm slices
2 cloves garlic, thinly sliced
200g cherry tomatoes
3 tbsp olive oil
2 tbsp red wine vinegar
300ml tomato passata
2 tbsp sultanas
1 tbsp capers, rinsed
2 tbsp pine nuts, toasted (optional)
small handful of basil leaves (optional)

Preheat the oven to 180°C fan/200°C/gas 6.

Toss the chopped vegetables into a high-sided roasting tray along with the cherry tomatoes, olive oil and red wine vinegar. Season with salt and pepper. Place the tray in the oven and roast for 30–40 minutes, giving it a stir halfway through so nothing burns, until the vegetables are starting to turn golden and soft.

Remove the tray from the oven and stir in the passata, sultanas and capers. Reduce the temperature to 160° fan/ 180°C/gas 4 and return to the oven for another 20 minutes until bubbling all over and slightly reduced.

Serve hot or at room temperature with toasted pine nuts and basil scattered over the top, if you like.

TIP: *A brilliant batch-cooking dish for busy weeks. I double up these quantities and roast it all in a large tray. Feel free to switch up the ingredients to use any leftover or lonely vegetables you have – better to use them than waste them. It also freezes well.*

Sweet and Smoky Bean Salad

Great bean salads remind me of childhood barbecues. It's a familiar staple and while I'd happily pick up a tub at my local deli, I realised I have rarely made one myself. So I played around with the ingredients and landed on this quick and tasty version. The key is the sweet and smoky dressing, so don't skip that part. Avocado is optional, but do try and buy the best-quality beans that you can as they will offer the best flavour.

(VEGAN) / GF / DF
Serves 4 as a side
Prep time: 15 mins

1 x 400g tin cooked white beans or chickpeas, drained and rinsed
1 x 400g tin cooked red kidney beans or black beans, drained and rinsed
50g sweetcorn
1 red pepper, deseeded and chopped into 1cm cubes (or you could substitute with some roasted peppers from a jar for a smokier flavour)
1 stick of celery, chopped into 1cm cubes
2 spring onions, trimmed and finely sliced
8 cherry tomatoes, cut into quarters
1 avocado, chopped into 1cm cubes (optional)
20g fresh coriander, chopped

For the dressing
2 tbsp olive oil
2 tbsp red wine vinegar
1 small clove garlic, grated
1 tsp honey (or maple syrup, if vegan)
½ tsp smoked paprika

Place all the salad ingredients in a large mixing bowl, and stir well.

To make the dressing, add all the ingredients to a small mixing bowl, season with salt and pepper to taste and stir well.

Stir the dressing into the bean salad, season well and serve.

TIP: *This is a great packed lunch dish to batch prepare at the start of the week. Just keep the avocado and dressing separate, adding them to that day's portion as you're packing it up. You could serve it with a green salad on the side.*

Black Rice and Greens with Sesame and Ginger Dressing

This is my idea of heaven on a plate. It's full of fresh flavours, and is both comforting and nurturing. The colour contrasts of the nutty black rice with the steamed crunchy greens is a gorgeous combination, and I guarantee the dressing will make your taste buds smile. I've added some toasted sesame seeds, chopped spring onion and coriander here, but sometimes I'll add a slice or two of firm tofu as well if I'd like to boost the protein per serving.

(VEGAN) / (GF) / DF
**Serves 2 as a main course or
4 as a side**
Prep time: 10 mins
Cook time: 5-10 mins (plus around
40-50 minutes for the black rice)

140g black rice
80g tenderstem broccoli
80g green beans
handful of peas (about 40g)

For the dressing
2 tbsp sesame oil
1 thumb-sized piece of fresh root
ginger, peeled and grated
(or 1½ tsp grated ginger)
2 tbsp tamari or soy sauce (use
tamari if gluten free)
juice of 1 lime
1 tsp honey (or maple syrup, if vegan)

To serve (optional)
1 tbsp toasted sesame seeds
1 spring onion, trimmed and sliced
handful of fresh coriander, roughly
chopped

Cook the black rice according to the packet instructions. (It takes longer to cook than regular rice so, if you're short for time, feel free to substitute for brown rice instead.)

To make the dressing, place all the ingredients in a clean jar with a lid and shake. Set aside.

Steam the broccoli and green beans for 4 minutes, adding the peas for the last 2 minutes, until they're lightly cooked but still vibrant green and crunchy.

Drain the cooked rice and stir in half the dressing, season with salt and pepper and pour onto a serving platter.

Top with the steamed greens, the rest of the dressing and scatter with sesame seeds, sliced spring onion and fresh coriander, if using. This can be served warm or cold.

TIP: *This dish is a wonderful side to prepare ahead and serve if you're entertaining, perhaps with some chicken, tofu or salmon cooked in the Miso Marinade on page 194.*

Courgette, Lemon and Almond Salad

This dish is fresh and light, with lots of lovely flavours yet only a few ingredients. From the charred courgettes, to the gentle nuttiness of almonds, to the zing of lemon, it is summer on a plate. It's a lovely quick lunch on its own, but I sometimes add goat's cheese or some smoked mackerel, leftover chicken or salmon, if I want to make it more filling. It also makes a happy side dish to other roasted meats or fish.

VEGAN / GF / DF
Serves 2 as a main or 4 as a side
Prep time: 5 mins
Cook time: 10-15 mins

2 medium courgettes, peeled into ribbons, or very thinly sliced
50g blanched almonds, toasted and roughly chopped
1 clove garlic, crushed
zest and juice of 1 lemon
2 tbsp extra-virgin olive oil
handful of fresh mint leaves, torn

Heat a griddle or frying pan over a high heat, then add the courgettes and griddle/fry on each side until you have distinct char lines, or they are nice and brown. If using a frying pan, add a splash of oil to stop them sticking.

Place the roughly chopped almonds, garlic, lemon zest and juice, olive oil and some salt and pepper in a large bowl and mix well.

As soon as the courgettes are cooked, add them into the bowl with the dressing and toss to coat.

Allow to cool, then scatter the mint leaves over and serve.

TIP: *If you need to toast the almonds, heat a dry frying pan and gently toast them for a couple of minutes until they are slightly golden. Remove them from the heat and put in a bowl to cool, otherwise they might burn.*

Kimchi and Feta Salad

A balanced and flavourful meal in five-ish minutes. Kimchi is a traditional, spicy, fermented Korean side dish and can be bought in most large supermarkets. Make sure you get fresh, refrigerated Kimchi rather than pasteurised, as the probiotic bacteria has potential benefits for gut health. I prefer toasted pumpkin seeds: you can buy them toasted or toast them quickly in a dry frying pan until they start to crackle. You can also replace the cabbage with lettuce if you'd prefer.

VEGETARIAN / GF
Serves 2
Prep time: 5-10 mins

¼ white cabbage, shredded
100g kimchi
2 tbsp pumpkin seeds, toasted
2 tbsp chopped fresh coriander
40g feta, crumbled
juice of ½ lemon
1 tbsp extra-virgin olive oil

Toss all the ingredients together in a salad bowl, season with salt and pepper and serve immediately.

TIP: *This recipe goes really well with the Black Rice and Greens with Sesame and Ginger Dressing on page 113 as part of a bigger spread.*

My Favourite Green Salad

I often suggest serving my recipes with a green salad, but someone recently wrote to me and said they never actually knew what to put into a green salad beyond lettuce. Good point! So here is the one that I make the most. Sweet crunchy leaves, creamy avocado, nutty seeds and then a sharp vinaigrette, which enhances whatever else it is being served with. The avocado is optional: you could add in some shaved fennel or sugar snap peas instead, for contrasting texture.

VEGETARIAN / (VEGAN) / GF / DF
Makes 2 large portions
Prep time: 10 mins

2 little gem lettuces or a small bag of
    mixed lettuce leaves
1 avocado, sliced
¼ cucumber, sliced
2 tbsp pumpkin seeds, toasted

For the dressing
1 tsp Dijon mustard
½ tsp honey (or maple syrup, if
    vegan)
1 tbsp apple cider vinegar (or white
    wine vinegar)
1 tbsp extra-virgin olive oil

Separate and wash the leaves, then pat dry and toss into salad bowl.

Scatter the avocado and cucumber over the leaves.

Place all the dressing ingredients in a clean jam jar, screw the lid on tightly and shake vigorously until combined.

Dress the salad, scatter over the pumpkin seeds and serve.

TIP: *Make lots of this dressing, as it'll keep in the fridge for a week and can be used to spruce up any other salads or vegetables.*

Harissa Roasted Vegetables

This versatile dish will happily take any vegetables that suit roasting, so feel free to swap around the ingredients according to what you have, and can easily be made ahead and reheated later in the week to eat for lunches or supper. It's a forgiving, mild recipe that pairs well with cheese. I've included feta, but it would also work well with goat's cheese, mozzarella, ricotta or grilled halloumi. Eggs, pre-cooked Puy lentils, meat and fish would work, too – a real all-rounder!

VEGETARIAN / GF / (DF)
Serves 2 as a main or 4 as a side
Prep time: 10 mins
Cook time: 50 mins

1 small aubergine, chopped into 2.5cm chunks
1 red pepper, chopped into 2.5cm chunks
1 courgette, chopped into 2.5cm chunks
1 small red onion, cut into 1cm slices
handful of cherry tomatoes
2 tsp harissa paste
1 tsp red wine vinegar
2 tbsp olive oil
40g feta, crumbled (optional)
handful of basil leaves, torn (optional)

Preheat the oven to 180°C fan/200°C/gas 6.

Place the aubergine, pepper, courgette, red onion and whole cherry tomatoes on a baking tray.

In a small bowl, mix the harissa, vinegar and oil, and season with salt and pepper, then rub this mixture all over the vegetables. Roast in the oven for 40–50 minutes, turning once or twice, until the veg is browned and soft.

Serve warm or cold with feta (or another cheese or accompaniment of your choice) and fresh basil to garnish.

TIP: *Another fantastic recipe for making the most of leftovers, as well as being a really useful dish to prepare ahead for busy weeks or healthy packed lunches. You could use the open jar of harissa paste to make the Spiced Slow-cooked Shoulder of Lamb on page 177.*

Roasted Cauliflower with Crispy Leaves, Green Lentils and Hazelnut Salsa

This delicious hazelnut salsa makes the simpler flavours of the cauliflower and lentils really sing, and it's a fibre-packed, filling and nourishing meal too. In the UK we tend to associate cauliflower with cheesy, creamy sauces, but try a different approach and you'll discover a hugely versatile ingredient whose texture and gentle flavour absolutely deserves to be centre stage every so often. You don't have to cook the lentils from scratch if you are short on time – just opt for pre-cooked lentils instead.

VEGETARIAN / (VEGAN) / GF/ DF
Serves 2 as a main or 4 as a side
Prep time: 10–15 mins
Cook time: 50 mins

120g dried green lentils, rinsed and
    drained (or 250g pre-cooked)
1 whole small cauliflower
2 tbsp olive oil

For the salsa
50g hazelnuts
large handful of parsley
1 small clove garlic
juice of ½ lemon
1 tsp Dijon mustard
1 tsp honey (or maple syrup, if vegan)
1 tbsp apple cider vinegar
4 tbsp extra-virgin olive oil

Preheat the oven to 200°C fan/220°C/gas 7.

Put the lentils on to boil and cook according to the packet instructions. Once cooked, drain and set aside. If using pre-cooked, rinse them well if in a tin or jar (no need if from a packet) and set aside.

Meanwhile, break the cauliflower into chunky florets, keeping the small leaves attached. Trim the stalk out of the larger leaves. Dress with the olive oil, season with salt and pepper and toss onto a baking tray. Roast for 30–40 minutes until the cauliflower is golden and the leaves have gone crispy.

While the cauliflower is roasting, tip the hazelnuts onto a small oven tray and roast in the oven for about 10 minutes until the skin is starting to split, then set aside to cool slightly. Set a timer, if necessary, as you don't want them to burn.

Blend the parsley, garlic, lemon juice, mustard, honey (or maple syrup), vinegar and olive oil for the salsa until mostly smooth. Add the toasted hazelnuts, season with salt and pepper and pulse to roughly chop them.

Place the cooked lentils on a serving platter, top with the roasted cauliflower and spoon over the salsa. Serve warm as it comes, or as a side to some meat, fish, or a fresh tomato salad.

> **TIP:** *A great dish for preparing ahead if you've got a busy week, as it makes a nutritionally complete meal on its own; plant-based protein from the lentils, vegetables, healthy fats from the hazelnuts and olive oil, and punchy flavour from the dressing. Great for packed lunches too.*

Tofu, Mushroom and Broccoli Traybake

This is a quick, wholesome weeknight supper and any leftovers are great eaten cold the next day. When it comes to tofu, texture is key – starting with a very firm one tends to be a good idea, as I find it's better for baking and roasting. Any variety of mushroom works here, but I go for a combination of oyster and chestnut, as I like their rich umami flavours. Serve with rice noodles or brown rice if you need a more filling meal.

VEGAN / GF / DF

Serves 2

Prep time: 5 mins (plus another 5 mins if you're making the marinade from scratch)

Cook time: 20 mins

150g mushrooms, halved
½ head of broccoli, broken into bitesize florets
200g very firm tofu, chopped into 2cm cubes
5 tbsp Miso Marinade (see page 194)
1 tsp sesame seeds
juice of 1 lime
1 spring onion, trimmed and finely sliced
½ chilli, finely sliced

Line a roasting tray with parchment paper.

Place the mushrooms, broccoli and tofu on the prepared roasting tray and pour over 4 tablespoons of the marinade. Give it a mix to make sure all the vegetables and tofu are well coated, then set aside for 2 hours if you have time (but don't worry too much if not as you'll still get good flavour).

Preheat the oven to 180°C fan/200°C/gas 6.

Roast the vegetables and tofu for 20 minutes, turning halfway through, until they are going crispy.

Meanwhile, mix the sesame seeds, lime juice and remaining tablespoon of marinade in a small bowl.

Pour the dressing over the vegetables and tofu, scatter the spring onion and sliced chilli on top and serve.

TIP: *You'll need to make the Miso Marinade on page 194 for this recipe. Use any leftovers to marinade some halved aubergines or chicken for later in the week.*

Vegetable Crumble

This is such a joy of a dish. As with so many of the recipes in this book, it is designed to be versatile, so use what vegetables you have to hand. Mushrooms and carrots with fresh tarragon is another variation I often make, for example. If you want to batch cook and freeze it, it's best to make (and freeze) the topping and base separately. Assemble and cook on the day you want to eat it.

VEGETARIAN / (VEGAN) / (GF) / (DF) / KIDS
Serves 4
Prep time: 15 mins
Cook time: 35 mins

1 tbsp olive oil
1 leek, trimmed and finely sliced
1 clove garlic, crushed
½ white or Savoy cabbage, outer leaves discarded, thickly sliced
1 tsp Dijon mustard
80ml cream (dairy or oat cream works best)
handful of frozen peas (about 40g)
½ × 400g tin of butter beans, drained and rinsed
squeeze of fresh lemon juice
2 tbsp chopped fresh parsley

For the crumble topping
2 tbsp wholegrain flour (use buckwheat or plain gluten-free, if necessary)
25g oats (use gluten-free, if necessary)
35g sunflower seeds
1 tbsp fridge cold butter, cubed (or use coconut oil, if vegan)
1 tsp mixed dried herbs
2 tbsp grated Cheddar (or vegan cheese)

Preheat the oven to 200°C fan/220°C/gas 7.

Place the olive oil in an ovenproof pan over a medium heat, add the leek and sauté for a few minutes until it begins to soften. Add the garlic and cook for a further 1–2 minutes. Mix in the cabbage and sauté for 2 minutes. Stir in the mustard, cream and a splash or two of water. Bring to a simmer.

Add the peas, beans, lemon juice and parsley, and stir well.

Remove from the heat and season to taste.

Measure all the crumble topping ingredients into a large mixing bowl. Rub the ingredients together using your fingertips to incorporate the butter.

Sprinkle the topping over the cabbage and bean mixture and cook in the oven for 25–30 minutes until bubbling and the topping is golden and crispy.

TIP: *Use the remaining ½ tin of butter beans to make a simple bean salad with some chopped cucumber, tomatoes, lemon juice, olive oil and fresh parsley.*

Baked Falafel

Warm and gently spiced falafel served with salad, tahini dressing, pickled veg and some chilli sauce is my go-to street food of choice – it has great flavour and texture, and it's got plentiful goodness in there, too. Here is my take on this much-loved Middle Eastern food hero. You can absolutely eat these as they come, but I like to serve them with a lovely tahini dressing (see page 134), My Favourite Green Salad (see page 117) and ripe tomatoes.

VEGAN / GF / DF / KIDS
Serves 2-3
Prep time: 15 mins
Cook time: 15-20 mins

olive oil, for greasing
1 × 400g tin of chickpeas, drained and rinsed
1 shallot or 1 small onion, roughly chopped
2 cloves garlic
2 tbsp roughly chopped fresh parsley
2 tbsp roughly chopped fresh coriander
1 tsp ground cumin
1 tsp ground coriander
1 tsp date syrup, honey or maple syrup
1 tbsp olive oil
80g dried polenta, to coat

Preheat the oven to 160°C fan/180°C/gas 4 and lightly oil a baking tray.

Place all the ingredients, except for the polenta and olive oil, in a food processor and blitz to form a rough paste.

Using wet hands (as it helps prevent the mixture sticking) roll the mixture into 10 small (5-6cm wide) patties, then roll them in the polenta.

Place the falafel patties on the prepared tray and drizzle over the olive oil. Bake in the oven for about 15-20 minutes until golden.

TIP: *Batch cook this recipe by doubling the quantities and freeze the patties before cooking (I do this on an oiled tray). Once frozen, tip them into a reusable bag and take out as many as required and cook them directly from frozen.*

Best Black Bean Burger

This is definitely the best bean burger I have made and I've made a lot! The recipe was inspired by a wonderful bean burger on Sally's Baking Addiction blog, but I've reduced the number of ingredients so it's more likely that you'll have everything to hand. Serve them with all the normal burger accompaniments and you'll never look back. It's also a family-friendly and economical option to have in the freezer to pull out whenever, so do make a few spare if possible.

(VEGETARIAN) / (GF) / KIDS
Makes 6
Prep time: 30–40 mins plus 2 hours resting in fridge
Cook time: 10–14 mins (grill), 20 minutes (baking)

2 × 400g tins of black beans, drained and rinsed
1 tbsp olive oil, plus extra for drizzling
½ red pepper, deseeded and roughly chopped
1 shallot or small onion, roughly chopped
220g mushrooms, roughly chopped
2 cloves garlic, crushed
1½ tsp ground cumin
½ tsp sweet smoked paprika
½ tsp dried mixed herbs
65g breadcrumbs (use gluten-free, if necessary)
80g feta, crumbled
1 large free-range egg
1 tbsp Worcestershire sauce (or a vegetarian alternative)

Preheat the oven to 150°C fan/170°C/gas 3.

Spread the drained beans on a baking tray and bake for 15 minutes until slightly dried out. (This is important, as a lower water content helps the beans to stick together better, and really improves the texture of the burger.)

Add the oil to a medium-large saucepan over a medium-high heat. Add the pepper, shallot or onion, mushrooms, garlic, cumin, paprika and mixed herbs and sauté for around 8 minutes until soft. Remove from the heat and set aside to cool a little.

Place the sautéed vegetables and all the remaining ingredients, including a good pinch of salt and grind of pepper, in a large food processor and pulse until combined, leaving some larger chunks. You don't want to end up with a paste, so go carefully. Using wet hands (as it helps prevent the mixture sticking), shape the mixture into 6 patties (each roughly 8–10cm). Line a baking tray with parchment paper and place the patties on top. Put the tray in the fridge for a couple of hours, to help the patties stick together.

Preheat the grill to a medium heat or the oven to 190°C fan 210°C/gas 7.

If grilling, drizzle a little olive oil over the patties and place them under the grill for 8 minutes. Turn them over, then grill for 4 minutes on the other side, checking every few minutes as every grill is different. They should look a little golden.

If baking, drizzle a little olive oil over the patties, then bake in the oven for 10 minutes. Flip them over and bake for a further 10 minutes.

Cheesy Baked Beans

I have a nostalgic soft spot for baked beans and this comforting, cheesy version is one I often turn to when I need to produce something warming and filling, fast. It's ended up becoming a bit of a winter staple in my home, as much a hit with children as with adults. I like to serve it with rocket or spinach scattered over the top, and a slice of rye or sourdough. Any leftovers are delicious for breakfast.

VEGETARIAN / GF / KIDS
Serves 4
Prep time: 5 mins
Cook time: 15-20 mins

1 stick of celery, diced
2 carrots, diced
1 shallot or 1 small onion, diced
1 tbsp olive oil
1 clove garlic, finely sliced
1 tbsp tomato purée
pinch of dried mixed herbs
1 x 400g tin of chopped tomatoes
2 x 400g tins of white beans (I like
   haricot or cannellini beans for this),
   drained and rinsed
50g mozzarella, grated or torn
50g Cheddar, grated

Place the celery, carrots, shallot or onion and olive oil in a large ovenproof frying pan (about 25–30cm) and sauté over a low-medium heat for about 10 minutes until soft, stirring occasionally.

Add the garlic, tomato purée and herbs, stir, and fry for a further 2 minutes.

Stir in the chopped tomatoes and beans and bring to a simmer. Allow to reduce slightly for 2–3 minutes.

Preheat the grill to high.

Season the beans with salt and pepper to taste, then scatter the cheeses over the top. Place under the grill until golden and bubbling on top.

TIP: *You'll need to make this in a large sauté or frying pan that can be placed under the grill (alternatively, make the beans in a large saucepan, then transfer to an ovenproof dish to finish under the grill).*

Freekeh with Crispy Roast Mushrooms

This dish requires minimal effort but delivers an abundance of flavour. I find the mushrooms get crispier if torn or broken rather than sliced, and it's easier, too. Freekeh is an ancient wholegrain made from green durum wheat, which is roasted and polished to remove the shells. It is similar in texture to bulgur wheat, but with a richer, nuttier flavour. You could swap it out for quinoa, bulgur wheat or wild / brown rice instead.

VEGAN / GF / DF / KIDS
Serves 4
Prep time: 5 mins
Cook time: 40-50 mins

400g (about 2 punnets) mixed mushrooms, roughly torn
2 shallots or 1 medium white onion, roughly sliced
1 clove garlic, crushed
1 tbsp olive oil
2 tbsp pumpkin seeds
160g freekeh, rinsed
1 tbsp finely chopped fresh parsley
1 tbsp tahini
zest and juice of 1 lemon
1 tsp tamari or soy sauce
1 tbsp warm water
Extra parsley leaves to garnish (optional)

Preheat the oven to 160°C fan/180°C/gas 4.

Scatter the torn mushrooms and sliced shallots or onion on a baking tray and dress with the olive oil, salt, pepper and garlic and mix well. Place in the oven and roast for 35-45 minutes, tossing or stirring occasionally, so the shallot or onion doesn't burn. Add the pumpkin seeds for the final 5 minutes.

Meanwhile, cook the freekeh according to the packet instructions. Drain and set aside to cool slightly before stirring through the chopped parsley.

In a small mixing bowl, mix the tahini and lemon juice. It will look like it's curdled but keep mixing until it forms a paste. Whisk in the tamari or soy sauce, lemon zest and water until smooth.

Scatter the freekeh on a serving plate, top with the mushrooms and dress with the tahini sauce. Garnish with some additional parsley leaves if you like.

TIP: *While you're waiting for the mushrooms to roast, you could make the most of the oven space and bake a seasonal frittata (see pages 90-4), or some breakfast muffins (see page 88) for the next day.*

One-pot Green Dahl

This is a one-pot wonder that we often make for Sunday night dinner at our house. Nourishing and wholesome, it really sets us up for the week ahead. I've added extra greens here with some Swiss chard, but you could easily swap this for spinach (a few cubes of frozen spinach would work well), beet leaves, cavolo nero, or even a couple of handfuls of peas, if that's what you have to hand.

VEGETARIAN / (VEGAN) / GF/ (DF)
Serves 4–6
Prep time: 5–10 mins
Cook time: 1 hr

1 shallot or 1 small white onion, sliced
1 tbsp coconut oil or mild olive oil
1 large piece of fresh root ginger (about 3cm), peeled and grated
2 cloves garlic, grated
1 green chilli, deseeded and chopped
1 tsp mustard seeds
1 tsp ground coriander
1 tsp ground cumin
1 tsp ground turmeric
300g dried black/brown lentils
1 × 400ml tin of coconut milk
200g Swiss chard, washed and roughly chopped
natural or dairy-free yoghurt, to serve (optional)
small handful of fresh coriander, chopped, to serve

In a shallow saucepan, fry the shallot or onion in the coconut or olive oil over a medium heat for 5 minutes until it starts to soften and caramelise, stirring occasionally.

Add the ginger, garlic and chilli and all of the spices, and fry for another 5 minutes, stirring often.

Mix in the lentils, coconut milk and 650ml water. Bring to the boil, reduce the heat and simmer for about 40–50 minutes, stirring occasionally, until the lentils are soft and the water absorbed.

Add the Swiss chard and cook for 5 minutes until wilted. Season to taste with salt and pepper.

Serve warm with a little yoghurt (or dairy-free alternative) swirled through, if you fancy, and coriander sprinkled on top.

TIP: *This recipe makes a versatile 'base' dahl to batch cook and freeze. Make it up to the point of adding the Swiss chard (but don't add it), then cool and freeze in portions. When you come to eat it, heat through with other fresh greens, roasted pumpkin, grated carrots or courgettes or any other vegetables you fancy.*

Pearl Barley and Courgette Risotto

I always think of making risotto as a mindful experience – the gentle stirring and slow adding of stock is soothing and provides a good opportunity to enjoy some peace and quiet. Pearl barley has a little bit more bite than risotto rice, so livens up this recipe. Mascarpone, lemon and basil do add a lovely depth of flavour, but if you wish to make this dairy free, replace the mascarpone for a vegan cream and use a dairy-free Parmesan for the topping.

VEGETARIAN / (VEGAN) / GF / (DF)
Serves 2-3
Prep time: 5 mins
Cook time: 1 hr

olive oil for frying
1 shallot or 1 small white onion, finely sliced
4 mushrooms (about 100g), finely diced
1 clove garlic, finely sliced
4 sprigs of thyme, leaves picked
250g pearl barley
50ml white wine
1.5 litres vegetable stock
2 medium courgettes (about 400g), cut into thin slices
zest and juice of 1 lemon
1 tbsp mascarpone (optional)
large handful of grated Parmesan (or pecorino or vegan Parmesan)
basil leaves, to serve

Place a heavy-based pan over a medium heat. Add the oil and shallot or onion and fry for about 3-4 minutes, stirring occasionally, until it is starting to caramelise. Add the mushrooms, garlic and thyme leaves and fry for another 5 minutes, stirring occasionally.

Add the pearl barley and fry for 2-3 minutes, stirring continuously, then pour in the white wine and allow to bubble briefly. Stir in enough vegetable stock to just cover the pearl barley, then turn down the heat and allow it to simmer, uncovered.

Keep topping up the risotto with stock as it absorbs into the grains, stirring from time to time to avoid it catching on the bottom of the pan. You'll need to do this intermittently until the barley is cooked through (about 35-40 minutes).

When the barley is almost cooked (it should be softened but still have a bit of chew), allow most of the remaining liquid to cook off (so the mixture isn't too wet), then add 3/4 of the courgettes, stir and simmer for a further 5 minutes until the courgette is just cooked through.

Finally, stir in the lemon zest and juice, mascarpone, if using, and season well with salt and pepper. Serve warm with Parmesan and basil leaves sprinkled over the top, along with the remaining courgettes.

TIP: *This risotto is not suitable for freezing, but it can be kept in the fridge for 2-3 days. Just keep the fresh basil and Parmesan separate until you're ready to serve. You can swap the courgettes for peas, spinach, grated carrots or beetroot, if you prefer.*

Easy Chickpea Pancakes

This is based on socca, a popular dish in the south of France. I like to serve these pancakes with smoked salmon, capers and cream cheese, or hummus and salad rolled into a savoury pancake wrap, or alongside some slices of ripe tomato, freshly ground pepper and a little good olive oil. Chickpea flour is higher in protein than other grain-based flours, as well as being a source of essential nutrients, including folate and magnesium – and it's gluten-free.

VEGAN/ GF/ DF/ (KIDS)
Makes 4
Prep time: 15 mins
Cook time: 16 mins

200g chickpea flour
½ tsp chilli flakes (optional)
2 tsp dried mixed herbs
1 tbsp olive oil, for frying

Sift the flour into a bowl. Pour in 300ml water and add the chilli flakes, herbs and a pinch of salt and pepper. Whisk everything together until smooth, then set aside and leave to thicken up for 5–10 minutes.

Heat the oil in a frying pan (about 26cm) over a medium-high heat.

Pour a quarter of the batter into the pan. If the mixture is quite thick, you may need to spread this around the pan with the back of a spoon. Cook for 2–3 minutes, or until the top is completely set and the bottom is golden brown. Carefully flip the pancake and cook for a further minute, until both sides are golden brown.

Repeat with the remaining batter.

Serve warm with your filling of choice, or store in an airtight container in the fridge for 2–3 days.

TIP: *Make a double batch of these pancakes, as they're really useful to have in the fridge to turn into a quick lunch, breakfast wrap or snack.*

Courgette, Lemon and Mozzarella Pasta

The lemony freshness of this light, summery pasta dish reminds me of long, lingering Mediterranean lunches with my family in Mallorca. It's simple to make and there are endless possibilities to add in more vegetables, or change the type of cheese and scatter with freshly torn herbs of choice. It's lovely as it is but if you want to make it more colourful, add some fresh or roasted cherry tomatoes, some rocket and a dollop of Cavolo Nero and Walnut Pesto (see page 192).

VEGETARIAN / (GF) / KIDS
Serves 2
Prep time: 5 mins
Cook time: 10-20 mins

180g pasta (use gluten-free,
 if necessary)
2 medium courgettes, cut into
 5mm-thick discs
1 tbsp extra-virgin olive oil, plus more
 to serve
1 tbsp pine nuts
1 clove garlic, crushed
zest and juice of ½ lemon
40g mozzarella, torn

Bring a large pan of salted water to the boil and cook the pasta according to the packet instructions.

Meanwhile, place the courgette and olive oil in a large frying pan over a medium heat and fry for 5 minutes. Add the pine nuts and garlic and fry for a further 2–3 minutes, stirring occasionally, until the courgette is starting to brown.

Remove from the heat and add the lemon zest and juice. Add the drained pasta and toss everything together.

Serve the courgette pasta with mozzarella scattered over the top and a drizzle of extra-virgin olive oil.

TIP: *Red lentil or chickpea pasta contains more protein than standard wheat pasta, which can help us feel fuller for longer, so is usually what I opt for when making this recipe.*

Fennel, Sardine and Sprouting Broccoli Pasta

This is a great dish if you wish to increase your oily fish intake during the week without spending a fortune on fresh fish. Sardines are considered a more sustainable choice than some other seafood. You can get some really delicious tinned or jarred sardines nowadays but if you don't like sardines, you could swap them for smoked mackerel, fresh salmon, or occasionally tinned or jarred tuna instead.

(GF) / DF
Serves 4
Prep time: 5 mins
Cook time: 20-25 mins

1 shallot or 1 small white onion, diced
1 small fennel bulb, thinly sliced
1 tbsp extra-virgin olive oil, plus more to serve
1 clove garlic, sliced
pinch of chilli flakes
200g sprouting (or tenderstem) broccoli, roughly chopped
50ml white wine
300g pasta (use gluten-free, if necessary)
1 × 120g tin of sardines, drained and bones removed if necessary
juice of 1 lemon

Gently fry the shallot or onion and fennel in the olive oil over a medium heat for about 10 minutes until softening and starting to caramelise.

Stir in the garlic and chilli flakes and fry for another 2 minutes.

Add the broccoli, white wine and a splash of water, cover with a lid and leave to steam for about 8 minutes.

Meanwhile, cook the pasta in a large pan of salted water according to the packet instructions.

Remove the lid from the broccoli, season with a little salt and add the sardines, along with a splash of the pasta cooking water, stirring so they break up into the sauce.

Add the cooked pasta, lemon juice and a generous drizzle of oil and stir.

Season with pepper and serve.

TIP: *I am generally opting for tinned sardines over tuna these days, as I'm conscious of how hard it is to check any sustainability claims made by the tuna industry. If I do buy a tin, I go for a brand that puts its good practices front and centre of their business.*

One-pot Lemon and Cabbage Spaghetti

I really love cabbage, so when I had some left in my fridge and it coincided with a pasta craving, this unusual – but brilliant – pairing was born. I urge you to give it a go, even if you're not sure you love cabbage. It might just convert you. The simplicity of this dish makes it a perfect weeknight meal: it is both nourishing and quick to make, allowing us the headspace to process the day's events whilst eating well – what's not to love?

VEGETARIAN / (GF) / KIDS
Serves 4
Prep time: 5 mins
Cook time: 15 mins

1.5 litres chicken or vegetable stock
250g spaghetti (e.g. wholegrain, lentil or brown rice)
½ white or green cabbage, finely sliced or shredded using a mandoline
50g Parmesan (or vegan Parmesan), grated (optional)
large handful of chopped fresh parsley
zest and juice of 1 lemon

Place the stock in a large pan and bring to a simmer over a medium heat.

Add the spaghetti and cook according to the packet instructions, adding the shredded cabbage for the last minute of the cooking time. (If needed, add more water to ensure the pasta is covered.)

Drain the spaghetti and cabbage, reserving some of the cooking liquid. Add the Parmesan, parsley and lemon zest and juice and stir well.

Season to taste with salt and pepper and serve.

TIP: A few capers and some rocket could be a nice addition if serving to friends. You could use the cabbage leftover from this recipe to make my Kimchi and Feta Salad (see page 116) or Vegetable Crumble (see page 126).

One-pan Mushroom and Leek Pasta

This is one of the most satisfying pasta dishes and I make it often. It tastes indulgent but is supremely fuss-free. Just roast everything in one tin, then stir in the cooked pasta and scatter some parsley over the top, which makes it look like it took more effort than it really did.

VEGETARIAN / (GF) / KIDS
Serves 2
Prep time: 8 mins
Cook time: 40–50 mins

1 punnet mushrooms (about 200g),
    sliced
½ leek, trimmed and sliced
1 medium courgette, sliced
olive oil, for drizzling
1 clove garlic, crushed
80g feta
½ tsp fresh or dried thyme leaves
200g pasta (use gluten-free,
    if necessary)
large handful of parsley, roughly
    chopped, to serve

Preheat the oven to 180°C fan/200°C/gas 6.

Place the mushrooms, leek and courgette in medium roasting dish (about 20 x 30cm). Drizzle with olive oil and add the garlic. Season with salt and pepper and mix to combine. Roast for 30–40 minutes, stirring occasionally, adding the thyme halfway through the cooking time, until all the vegetables are soft and starting to brown.

Remove the dish from the oven and place the feta (no need to chop or break it up) amongst the vegetables. Bake for a further 10 minutes.

Meanwhile, cook the pasta according to the packet instructions. Drain and reserve some of the cooking water.

Stir the cooked pasta into the veggies and feta. Mix well, adding a splash of pasta water, if necessary, and serve.

Tip: *You can use this method for any combination of vegetables. It's a great way to use up any lonely veg you have lurking in the fridge.*

One-pan Roasted Salmon, Fennel and Potatoes with Tarragon Sauce

When you want to serve something that's special but still simple, this one-pot salmon dish is a must. I make it when I've got a little time on my side, but minimal energy left (and therefore don't want a lot of fiddly prep or a huge pile of washing up). It's mostly a case of chopping, roasting and waiting, and you're rewarded with a wonderful weeknight meal.

GF / (DF)
Serves 2
Prep time: 10 mins
Cook time: 1 hr 25 mins

1 leek, trimmed and cut into
   1cm rounds
2 sticks of celery, chopped into
   1cm pieces
1 fennel bulb, cut into 1cm wedges
   (reserve any fronds to garnish)
4 waxy potatoes (such as Charlotte,
   Jersey Royals or Maris Peer), cut
   into 1cm rounds.
½ lemon, cut into thinnest possible
   slices and seeds removed
2 tbsp olive oil
100ml chicken or vegetable stock
2 salmon fillets (or hot-smoked
   salmon fillets)

For the tarragon sauce
2 tbsp crème fraîche (or dairy-free
   alternative such as oat crème
   fraîche, coconut cream or dairy-
   free yoghurt)
juice of ½ lemon
1 tsp horseradish sauce
2 tbsp chopped tarragon leaves
1 tsp Dijon mustard

Preheat the oven to 140°C fan/160°C/gas 3.

Toss all the chopped vegetables and lemon slices into a baking dish with the olive oil and season with salt and pepper. Cover with a lid and bake in the oven for 50 minutes until the veg is soft.

Meanwhile, make the sauce. Mix the crème fraîche with the lemon juice, horseradish, tarragon and mustard, season and set aside.

Remove the vegetables from the oven and increase the temperature to 200°C fan/220°C/gas 7. Stir the vegetables, then return to the oven for a further 20 minutes without the lid, until starting to brown and crisp.

Remove the dish from the oven and pour the stock into the base, then carefully place the salmon fillets on top of the vegetables. Bake without the lid for 12–15 minutes, or until the fish is just cooked through. (If using hot-smoked salmon, bake with the lid on for 6–8 minutes so the fish warms through without drying out.) Garnish with the fennel fronds, if you have some.

Serve hot with a bowl of the tarragon sauce on the side.

TIP: *Make the most of the oven being on, and add another tray of vegetables to roast, or a couple of small jacket potatoes.*

Quick Fish Pie

This is a great family classic, but when made the traditional way, I find it quite time-consuming to prepare, so it's not really a viable weekday meal. In this recipe, I've sped up the process, cheating a little on the white sauce, and using a great method of grating everything together (a brilliant technique learnt from a Jamie Oliver recipe). Now we can enjoy this comforting pie without all the fuss.

GF / (DF) / KIDS
Serves 6
Prep time: 20 mins
Cook time: 40 mins

180g crème fraîche (or use a dairy-
  free alternative, such as oat cream)
1 tsp Dijon mustard
1 tbsp chopped fresh dill
1 tbsp chopped fresh parsley
1 clove garlic, grated
1 courgette, grated
1 small leek, trimmed and grated
3 handfuls (about 120g) frozen peas
2 large handfuls of spinach
  (about 40g)
800g raw fish pie mix (I used salmon,
  prawns and cod)
2 large potatoes (about 600g), grated
3 tbsp olive oil
20g Cheddar, grated (optional)

Preheat the oven to 180°C fan/200°C/gas 6.

In a large bowl, mix together the crème fraîche, mustard, dill, parsley and garlic.

Add the courgette, leek, peas, spinach and fish, and gently toss so everything is coated with the sauce. Tip into a baking dish and level the surface.

Mix the potatoes with a drizzle of the olive oil and the Cheddar, if using. Season with salt and pepper and use to top the fish mixture. Drizzle the remaining olive oil over the top. Bake in the oven for 40 minutes until bubbling and the top is crisping up and golden.

Quick Fish Curry

This is exactly the kind of soothing and heart-warming plate of food I look forward to after a busy day. You could use red or yellow curry paste, instead of green, depending on your personal preference. If you want to change things up further, it also works well with strips of chicken breast instead of fish. Similarly, if you have roast chicken leftovers, this is a great way to turn it into a completely new meal. Serve with rice, potatoes or vegetables.

GF / DF
Serves 4
Prep time: 5 mins
Cook time: 20-25 mins

1 × 400ml tin of coconut milk
½ tsp fish sauce
handful of trimmed green beans
    (about 100g)
4 skinless white fish fillets (I use cod,
    but ling or tusk are great value and
    can be more sustainable options)
1 lime, cut into wedges
handful of fresh coriander leaves

For the spice mixture
1 tbsp coconut oil (or light olive oil)
2 tbsp Thai green curry paste
1 tsp mustard seeds
½ tsp ground turmeric
1 shallot or 1 small white onion,
    roughly chopped
1 small piece of fresh root ginger
    (about 2.5cm), peeled and grated
1 clove garlic, crushed
2 makrut lime leaves (or lime zest and
    juice if you don't have lime leaves)

To make the spice mixture, melt the coconut oil in a large saucepan or sauté pan over a low heat. Add all the remaining ingredients and fry gently for 4 minutes.

Pour the coconut milk and fish sauce into the pan with the spice mixture and simmer for 5 minutes. Add the green beans and cook for a further 3 minutes.

Place the fish fillets on top of the sauce and cover the pan with a lid. Turn down the heat and allow it to simmer gently for about 10 minutes, depending on the thickness of the fish. It should be just opaque all the way through.

Serve with a squeeze of lime and a sprinkling of fresh coriander leaves.

TIP: *You can use this sauce for chicken, salmon, tofu or chickpeas.*

Salmon and Soba Noodles with Peanuts

Fresh, fast and filling, this meal is a big bowlful of flavour. Once you've cooked the salmon and soba noodles, it's a very quick assembly job before serving up and tucking in. The peanuts can be swapped for cashews (or seeds, if you're nut free) or left out entirely if you prefer. And the salmon could be swapped for trout or another fish of your choice, depending on what's available and what you enjoy eating.

GF / DF
Serves 2
Prep time: 10 mins
Cook time: 10 mins

1 small piece of fresh root ginger (about 2.5cm), peeled and finely grated

1 tbsp tamari (or soy sauce)

2 salmon fillets

juice of 2 limes, plus extra wedges to serve (optional)

2 tbsp sesame oil (or mild olive oil)

1 tsp honey

large pinch of chilli flakes

½ cucumber, sliced in half lengthways, deseeded and chopped into roughly 1cm cubes

4 radishes, thinly sliced

1 spring onion, trimmed and thinly sliced

50g peanuts, roughly chopped

100g soba noodles

10g coriander leaves

In a small bowl, mix the ginger with the tamari (or soy sauce), then rub this over the salmon and set aside.

In a large bowl, combine the lime juice, sesame (or olive) oil, honey and chilli flakes. Add the cucumber and mix into the dressing. Add the radishes, spring onion and peanuts and toss everything together with a generous pinch of salt and pepper until evenly coated. Set aside.

Preheat the grill to medium.

Grill the salmon, skin side down for 8-10 minutes until just cooked.

Meanwhile, bring a large pan of salted water to the boil and cook the soba noodles according to the packet instructions. Rinse them well with cold water once cooked, drain and immediately toss with the cucumber mixture, so that everything is well mixed.

Place the noodle and cucumber salad onto individual plates or a serving platter and flake the cooked salmon over the top.

Scatter with the coriander leaves and serve with extra wedges of lime, if you like.

TIP: *If making this ahead for a packed lunch or doing some meal prep, omit the cucumber (it goes a bit soggy if left) or use sugar snap peas or celery instead. It tastes just as good cold as it does hot.*

Summer Vegetable and Fish Stew with Aioli

This is a gorgeous summery dish that is lovely for slightly cooler evenings. The trick is the texture – you want all the vegetables to be cooked through but still chunky and holding their shape, rather than disintegrating. That's why it's important to use a waxy potato that doesn't fall apart and to add the cherry tomatoes closer to the end, so they don't dissolve into the sauce. You can substitute other vegetables, like peas, beans, or courgettes.

GF / DF
Serves 2
Prep time: 10 mins
Cook time: 40-45 mins

1 tbsp olive oil, for frying
1 stick of celery, chopped into
    1-2cm chunks
1 carrot, chopped into 1-2cm chunks
1 small fennel bulb, chopped into
    1-2cm chunks (reserve any fronds
    to garnish)
1 small leek, trimmed and cut into
    1-2cm discs
300ml chicken or vegetable stock
2 medium (about 240g) waxy
    potatoes (such as Charlotte, Jersey
    Royal, or Maris Peer), chopped into
    1-2cm chunks
10 cherry tomatoes
1 tbsp finely chopped fresh parsley
1 tbsp finely chopped fresh chives
2 skinless white fish fillets, chopped
    into 5cm pieces
1 lemon, cut into wedges to serve

For the aioli
1 egg yolk
1 clove garlic, crushed
zest and juice of 1 lemon
1 heaped tsp Dijon mustard
50ml mild olive oil

In a heavy-based pan with a lid (I use a large casserole dish), pour a generous glug of olive oil. Add the celery, carrot, fennel and leek and sauté over a low-medium heat for 10-15 minutes stirring occasionally to avoid them catching and burning, until starting to soften.

Pour in the stock and turn down to a very gentle simmer. Stir in the potatoes, cover with a lid and cook for about 12-15 minutes until the potato feels almost done. Add the cherry tomatoes, cover again and simmer for a further 5 minutes.

Meanwhile, make the aioli in a small mixing bowl. Whisk together the egg yolk, garlic, lemon zest and juice and Dijon mustard. Very slowly start pouring in the oil little by little, whisking vigorously the whole time, until you have a lovely thick, smooth aioli. Season with salt and pepper.

Stir the parsley and chives into the stew, season with salt and pepper, then sit the pieces of fish on the surface. Cover with a lid and steam the fish for about 5 minutes until just cooked through.

Serve immediately with more lemon juice squeezed over, a spoon of aioli and any fennel fronds you have scattered over the top.

Chicken, Courgette and White Bean Stew

Comforting and light but deep in flavour, this is an easy, nourishing dish for any night of the week. It's a nutritionally balanced meal, too, delivering on fibre from the vegetables and protein thanks to the beans and chicken. I sometimes serve this with a crisp salad or steamed greens, but more often than not we just eat it as it comes. If you'd like to freeze it, strip the chicken meat from the bones first and it'll be fine for up to 3 months.

GF / DF / KIDS
Serves 4
Prep time: 10 mins
Cook time: 45–50 mins

2 tbsp olive oil
8 chicken drumsticks or thighs
1 small onion, finely sliced
1 clove garlic, finely sliced
2 sticks of celery, finely sliced
splash of white wine
1 tbsp tarragon leaves
1 × 400g tin of white beans, drained and rinsed (I use butter beans or cannellini)
2 medium courgettes, cut into 1cm discs
250ml chicken stock
1 lemon, to serve (optional)

Preheat the oven to 180°C fan/200°C/gas 6.

Place a casserole or ovenproof pan over a high heat. Add the oil and gently brown the chicken pieces until golden. Remove from the pan and set aside.

Add the onion, garlic and celery to the pan, reduce the heat and fry gently for 10 minutes, adding a little more olive oil, if needed.

Once the onion and garlic are translucent and soft, return the chicken to the pan, add the wine, tarragon, beans, courgettes and chicken stock. Cover with a lid and bake in the oven for 30 minutes until bubbling all over and the chicken is browned and cooked through.

Serve in bowls with lots of the juices and a squeeze of fresh lemon juice, if using.

Chicken, Leek and Mushroom Pie

There is something supremely cosy and nostalgic about a pastry-topped pie, but if you'd prefer to leave the pastry out then it works just as well with thinly sliced (or mashed) white or sweet potatoes instead. If you opt for shop-bought puff pastry, look out for one made with all butter and recognisable ingredients on the label. Dorset Pastry is my favourite. This is delicious served with a crispy salad. If you don't like tarragon, you can use parsley instead.

(GF) / (DF) / KIDS
Serves 4–5
Prep time: 10 mins
Cook time: 1 hr 10 mins

1 shallot or small white onion, roughly chopped
2 tbsp olive oil
1 punnet of mushrooms (about 200g), sliced
2 cloves garlic, finely sliced
100ml white wine
200ml chicken stock
2 leeks, trimmed and cut into 1cm rounds
2 tbsp crème fraîche (or soy / oat cream)
2 tbsp picked tarragon leaves
1 tsp Dijon mustard
juice of ½ lemon
400g cooked chicken, torn into bitesize pieces (this is roughly ½ a medium roast chicken)
200g peas (about 2 big handfuls)
1 x 320g packet of ready-rolled all-butter puff pastry (if dairy or gluten-free, use thinly sliced potatoes instead)
1 free-range egg, beaten
pinch of fennel seeds

Preheat the oven to 180°C fan/200°C/gas 6.

In a large shallow casserole, ovenproof frying pan or saucepan, gently fry the chopped shallot or onion in the olive oil over a medium heat for about 5 minutes. Add the mushrooms and garlic and fry for a further 10 minutes, stirring every now and then.

Pour in the wine and let it bubble for 1–2 minutes, before adding the chicken stock and leeks. Allow to simmer, uncovered, for about 10 minutes until the liquid has reduced by about half.

Stir in the crème fraîche (or soy/oat cream), tarragon, mustard and lemon juice, then add the cooked chicken and peas and stir again well.

Transfer the chicken mixture to an ovenproof pie dish, if necessary, then top the dish with the pastry, trimming around the edge and pressing the edges with a fork to seal in the filling. Make a 1cm cut in the middle of the pastry to allow steam to escape and brush the pastry with beaten egg, scatter a few fennel seeds over the top and bake for 30–40 minutes until the pastry is golden and the filling is bubbling.

TIP: *You can make the filling ahead – either the day before and keep it in the fridge, or in the freezer for up to 3-4 months. This is a great recipe to use up any leftover roasted chicken (or festive turkey), but you can use pre-cooked chicken or a rotisserie chicken, if you'd prefer.*

One-pot Lemongrass Roasted Chicken and Rice

This is an incredibly low-maintenance dish. It involves one pot (so minimal clearing up) and is a great weeknight meal if you have friends over. If you don't have time to make the marinade paste, you can sub this for a good-quality shop-bought Thai curry (or other curry) paste and it will still taste wonderful. If you're making this for kids, you can omit the chilli. I serve it with some simple steamed greens, such as bok choy or tenderstem broccoli.

GF / DF / KIDS
Serves 4
Prep time: 10 mins
Cook time: 50 mins

8 skinless chicken thighs
170g basmati rice
330ml chicken stock
80ml coconut milk
dash of fish sauce
handful of fresh coriander
1 lime, cut into wedges

For the marinade
2 thumb-sized pieces of fresh root
    ginger, peeled
3 cloves garlic
small bunch of fresh coriander
1 green chilli, deseeded
4 fresh lime leaves or zest of 1 lime
1 lemongrass stalk, tough outer layer
    removed
1 tbsp mild olive oil
½ tsp ground turmeric
½ tsp coriander seeds
¼ tsp ground cumin
pinch of salt

Preheat the oven to 180°C fan/200°C/gas 6.

Roughly chop and blitz all the marinade ingredients in a small food processor or electric spice grinder, adding a dash of coconut milk or water so it blends into a smooth paste.

Rub the marinade all over the chicken thighs and place them in a small-medium ovenproof dish or roasting tray. You want the thighs to fit snugly in the dish. Roast the chicken thighs in the oven for 20 minutes.

Remove the tray from the oven, lift out the chicken thighs and set aside on a plate. Add the uncooked rice to the chicken roasting tray.

Place the stock and coconut milk in a small saucepan and bring to the boil. Pour this mixture over the rice, add a dash of fish sauce and a pinch of salt, then return the chicken thighs on top. Return the whole lot to the oven and roast for another 30 minutes, or until the rice is cooked through and the chicken is falling off the bone.

Serve with fresh coriander and wedges of lime.

TIP: *If you want to prepare this ahead, make the marinade and rub it onto the chicken, then place covered in the fridge until you're ready to cook. You can also double up this marinade and freeze half for another day.*

Turkey Burgers

It is well worth doubling or tripling the recipe for these burgers and freezing some, as they are a great solution when you're having a last-minute BBQ or needing to feed a lot of hungry mouths. Serve them traditional-style in a bun piled with the usual burger accompaniments, or they are lovely with a great salad or some cooked vegetables. I've been making turkey burgers for years and they are such a satisfying meal for adults and kids alike.

GF / DF / KIDS
Makes 4
Prep time: 5 mins
Cook time: 25-30 mins

1 red onion, finely diced
3 tbsp olive oil
1 clove garlic, crushed
1 tsp dried mixed spices
1 tsp smoked paprika
500g turkey mince

Gently fry the diced onion in 1 tablespoon of the olive oil over a low heat for about 10 minutes until softening and starting to brown. Add the garlic and spices and fry for another 2 minutes, stirring occasionally. Remove from the heat and set aside to cool completely.

In a large bowl, mix together the turkey mince, onion mixture and a good pinch of salt and pepper. Using wet hands (as it helps prevent the mixture sticking), shape the mixture into 4 patties (you could make 8 smaller patties if you're cooking for children).

Place the remaining olive oil in a large pan over a medium heat, add the patties and cook for 6-8 minutes on each side until golden brown and cooked through.

TIP: *These are great for the freezer and a saviour for busy weeknights. Freeze uncooked, flat on an oiled baking tray, then transfer them to a labelled, sealed bag once frozen solid. This saves space and maintains good freezer hygiene as it is raw poultry. Defrost thoroughly before cooking.*

Turkey Ragù

Spaghetti Bolognese is ingrained into our collective consciousness as a weeknight staple, but I've been enjoying the switch to making a hearty pasta sauce with turkey mince (rather than beef) recently. I also regularly make a vegan version by swapping out the turkey and chicken stock altogether for chopped mushrooms, lentils and vegetable stock. If you don't want to eat this alongside pasta, however, it's also lovely with steamed green beans and broccoli, or in a baked potato.

GF / (DF) / KIDS
Serves 4-6
Prep time: 10 mins
Cook time: 45 mins-1 hr

2 tbsp olive oil
1 leek, trimmed and roughly diced
1 shallot or small white onion, roughly diced
1 small fennel bulb, roughly diced
1 stick of celery, roughly diced
2 cloves garlic, crushed
½ tsp ground nutmeg
1 bay leaf
1 tsp fresh thyme leaves (or ½ tsp dried thyme / dried mixed herbs)
handful of cherry tomatoes, quartered
500g turkey mince
100ml white wine
300ml chicken stock
1 tsp Worcestershire sauce
juice of ½ lemon
handful of fresh parsley, finely chopped
pecorino or Parmesan, grated, to serve (optional)

Heat the olive oil in a heavy-based pan over a medium heat. Add the leek, shallot, fennel and celery and sauté for about 8-10 minutes, stirring often, until the vegetables have softened and the onion is turning translucent. Add the garlic, nutmeg, bay leaf, thyme and cherry tomatoes, turn up the heat and cook for a couple of minutes so the vegetables start to turn a little golden and caramelise, stirring regularly.

Push the vegetables to the sides of the pan and add the turkey mince. Brown the mince, breaking it up with the back of a wooden spoon.

Once the turkey is browned, season with salt and pepper, add the wine and stir, scraping everything off the bottom of the pan. Pour in the stock, stir and simmer gently for 30-40 minutes until the liquid has reduced by about half.

Just before serving, add the Worcestershire sauce, lemon juice, stir in the parsley and grate over the pecorino or Parmesan, if using.

TIP: *Perfect batch-cooking food, I'd highly recommend doubling or tripling this recipe and freezing it ready-cooked into handy portions for another day.*

Lamb Larb

This recipe is inspired by my love of vibrant Thai salads. The combination of herbs and spices here is the perfect complement to the indulgent flavours of lamb. Serve in crisp, fresh lettuce cups on a summer's evening.

GF / DF
Serves 2
Prep time: 5–10 mins
Cook time: 15 mins

1 shallot, finely diced
1 red chilli, deseeded and finely chopped
1 small piece of fresh root ginger (about 2.5cm), peeled and grated
1 clove garlic, crushed
2 tbsp sesame oil (or 1 tbsp mild olive oil)
300g lamb mince
1 spring onion, trimmed and thinly sliced
dash of fish sauce
1 tsp honey
zest and juice of 1 lime
a few picked leaves of coriander, dill and mint, to serve
2 little gem lettuces, leaves separated, to serve

In a large frying pan, sauté the shallot, chilli, ginger and garlic in 1 tablespoon of the oil for about 4 minutes over a medium heat, until starting to soften.

Add the lamb mince, breaking it up with the back of a wooden spoon, and fry for a few minutes until the lamb is cooked through, stirring so all the mince is mixed through the shallot mixture. Turn up the heat and crisp up the mince for a further 5 minutes or so. Stir occasionally to prevent it catching on the bottom of the pan.

Remove from the heat and stir in the spring onion, fish sauce, 1 tablespoon of sesame oil (no need to add extra oil here if you're using olive oil as it's mostly for flavour), honey, lime zest and juice, and season to taste with salt and pepper.

Serve with the fresh herbs scattered over the top and the lettuce cups on the side.

TIP: *This recipe calls for lamb mince, but beef, pork or turkey mince would work, too.*

Pork and Fennel Meatballs in Tomato Sauce

This fragrant combination of pork and fennel is a classic for good reason. The fennel seeds cut through the rich meaty flavour and bring an aromatic frisson to this dish. I like to double up when making this and keep some in the freezer for busy days. You can substitute the pork mince for beef or turkey, if you'd prefer.

GF / (DF) / KIDS
Serves 4
Prep time: 5 mins
Cook time: 1 hr–1 hr 5 mins

2 small shallots or 1 medium onion, diced
1 tbsp olive oil
1 clove garlic, crushed
1 tsp fennel seeds
1 tsp dried mixed herbs
pinch of chilli flakes
½ tsp grated nutmeg
500g pork mince
1 × 400g tin of white beans, drained and rinsed
1 red onion, thinly sliced
1 × 400g tin of chopped tomatoes
1 tbsp sherry vinegar
pinch of chilli flakes or a dash of Worcestershire sauce (optional)
handful of fresh basil leaves
Parmesan, grated to serve (optional)

In a large saucepan, fry the shallot or onion gently in the olive oil over a medium heat for 6–8 minutes, then add the garlic, fennel seeds, herbs, chilli flakes and nutmeg and season with salt and pepper. Fry for a further couple of minutes, stirring occasionally, to release the aromatic flavours of the herbs. Remove from the heat and set aside to cool.

Mix the fried shallot mixture into the pork mince. Season again with a pinch of salt and pepper. Using wet hands (as it helps prevent the mixture sticking), roll the mixture into 16 golf-ball-sized rounds.

Preheat the grill to medium and the oven to 160°C fan/ 180°C/gas 4.

Place the meatballs in one layer on a roasting tray and grill for about 10 minutes until the tops are starting to brown.

Add the beans, thinly sliced red onion, tomatoes, vinegar and chilli flakes or Worcestershire sauce, if using, to the tray with the meatballs and transfer to the oven to roast for 40–45 minutes until the sauce is bubbling.

Sprinkle with the basil leaves and grated Parmesan, if using, to serve.

Slow-cooked Beef Massaman

This dish needs time to let all its aromatic flavours intermingle and for the beef to become tender while retaining its moisture. Stick on the slow-cooker when you head out for the day and you'll return home to a warm and hearty plate of food when you need it most. You can of course cook this at a low temperature in a conventional oven, but you can't leave it to its own devices in quite the same way.

GF / DF
Serves 4
Prep time: 15 mins
Cook time: 6 hrs 30 mins (slow-cooker); 4 hrs 30 mins (oven)

2 tbsp massaman paste
1 tbsp crunchy peanut butter (or 2 tbsp whole unsalted peanuts, chopped)
1 × 400ml tin of coconut milk
2 makrut lime leaves or zest of 1 lime
400g stewing beef (such as chuck or shin), chopped into 5cm pieces
3 small shallots, sliced in half lengthways
300g whole baby potatoes
1 red pepper, deseeded and sliced
100g green beans, halved
juice of 1 lime
½ tsp fish sauce
fresh coriander leaves, to serve

TIP: *This is minimal effort in terms of preparation time, but you'll need to plan ahead as it takes 6.5 hours to cook. If batch cooking, freeze in portions once cooked, but before adding the lime juice and fresh coriander.*

To make in a slow-cooker:

Add the massaman paste, peanut butter (or peanuts) and 200ml hot water to the slow-cooker (before turning it on) and whisk until smooth. Stir in the coconut milk and lime leaves, then add the stewing beef, shallots, potatoes and a pinch of salt. Slow cook on low for 6 hours.

Add the red pepper and beans, stir them in, and cook for a further 30 minutes.

Turn off the heat and stir in the lime juice and fish sauce. Adjust the seasoning to taste and serve with fresh coriander scattered over the top.

To make in a conventional oven:

Preheat the oven to 150°C fan/170°C/gas 3.

In a large casserole, whisk the massaman paste, peanut butter (or peanuts), coconut milk and lime leaves with 200ml hot water until smooth. Add the beef, shallots, potatoes and a pinch of salt, cover with a tight-fitting lid and cook for 1 hour.

Turn down the temperature to 120°C/140°C/gas 1 and cook for another 3 hours.

Add the pepper and green beans, stir, and cook for a further 30 minutes.

Remove from the oven and stir in the lime juice and fish sauce. Adjust the seasoning to taste and serve with fresh coriander scattered over the top.

Spiced Slow-cooked Shoulder of Lamb

Just gather up the ingredients into the slow-cooker and get on with something else (although it can also be slow-cooked in an oven if preferred). I prefer to trim off and discard any visible fat from the lamb before I start to cook, or I find the dish can be a bit too fatty once cooked. Serve it with some wholewheat couscous or quinoa or a big crunchy slaw and some flatbreads or pitta.

GF / DF
Serves 6
Prep time: 10 mins
Cook time: 8 hrs (slow-cooker);
  5–6 hrs (oven)

3 carrots, cut into 2cm rounds
2 sticks of celery, chopped into
  1cm pieces
3 shallots or 1 medium white onion,
  roughly sliced
2 cloves garlic, sliced
1.2–1.4kg shoulder of lamb, bone-in
  (or use an equivalent-sized leg of
  lamb, if preferred), trimmed of any
  visible fat.
100ml white wine
200ml chicken or vegetable stock
2 bay leaves
1 tsp dried mixed herbs
1 cinnamon stick (or ½ tsp ground
  cinnamon)
1–2 tbsp harissa paste (I use rose
  harissa, which is lovely)
8 dried apricots, roughly chopped
2 tbsp chopped fresh parsley,
  to serve

To make in a slow-cooker:

Place all the ingredients (apart from the apricots and parsley) in a slow-cooker. Vary the amount of harissa depending on how much spice you enjoy. Add a decent pinch of salt and a good grind of black pepper. Turn the cooker to its high setting and cook for about 8 hours until the meat is falling off the bone.

Once cooked, use two forks to shred the meat off the shoulder joint, discarding any bones or skin. Stir the shredded meat, along with the chopped apricots through the veggies and sauce. Season again to taste and add the chopped fresh parsley just before serving.

To make in a conventional oven:

Preheat the oven to 150°C fan/170°C/gas 3.

Place all the ingredients (apart from the apricots and parsley) in a large casserole cooker, nestling the vegetables around meat. Vary the amount of harissa depending on how much spice you enjoy. Add a decent pinch of salt and a good grind of black pepper, then cover with a tight-fitting lid. Cook for 1 hour.

Turn the oven temperature down to 120°C fan/140°C/gas 1 and cook for a further 4–5 hours until the meat is falling off the bone. Spoon the juices over the lamb a couple of times while cooking, to help keep it tender.

Once cooked, use two forks to shred the meat off the shoulder joint, discarding any bones or skin. Stir the shredded meat, along with the chopped apricots through the veggies and sauce. Taste and adjust the seasoning as necessary. Sprinkle with the parsley just before serving.

Seedy Crackers

These crunchy crackers are incredibly simple to make and satisfying on their own or topped with hummus, mackerel pâté or with dips of any kind. My daughter and I really enjoy making them together – there's something about sprinkling in all the seeds and then stirring up and rolling a dough that we both find very satisfying. Great for a picnic, on a cheeseboard or in a packed lunch. You can always switch around the seeds according to what you have to hand.

VEGAN / DF / KIDS
Makes roughly 10 long crackers
Prep time: 5 mins (plus 30 mins resting time)
Cook time: 20 mins

100g wholemeal flour (I use spelt) , plus extra for dusting
2 tbsp pumpkin seeds
2 tbsp sunflower seeds
1 tsp sesame seeds
1 tsp flaxseeds
1 tsp nigella seeds
1 tsp poppy seeds
¼ tsp salt
2 tbsp olive oil

Combine the flour, seeds and salt in a bowl. Add the oil and 50ml water and mix to a firm but pliable dough (you may need to add slightly more flour or more water, depending on the type of flour used).

Rest the dough, covered, in the fridge for 30 minutes.

Preheat the oven to 160°C fan/180°C/gas 4 and line a baking sheet with parchment paper.

To roll the crackers, take a thumb-size piece of the dough and make it into a sausage shape with your hands. Roll the sausage on a floured surface with a rolling pin until the dough is about 1mm thick (it should be about 20×6cm). Carefully move the rolled dough onto the prepared sheet and repeat. (You'll probably need a couple of baking sheets or cook them in batches.)

Bake on a high shelf in the oven for 15–20 minutes until the crackers start to turn golden.

Once cooked, leave on the baking sheet for a few minutes, then transfer to a wire rack to cool.

Store in an airtight container for up to 2 weeks.

TIP: *I think these would make a very welcome homemade gift, with some lovely cheese, wrapped up in parchment paper and tied with some string.*

Chickpea Mayo

Chickpeas and mayonnaise don't immediately sound appetising but, trust me, it's delicious! Serve with a salad, spread onto crispbreads, rolled up into a wholemeal wrap with crunchy lettuce or over a baked potato. Sometimes I add fresh, roughly chopped parsley, rocket and tinned sweetcorn, too. It will be fine in the fridge for 4–5 days, so it's great for packed lunches.

VEGETARIAN / GF / DF / KIDS
Serves 4 as an accompaniment to crackers or toast, or 2 as a main
Prep time: 5 mins

1 × 400g tin of chickpeas, drained and rinsed
½ red onion, finely diced (or 2 spring onions, finely sliced)
2 tbsp mayonnaise
1 tbsp olive oil
zest and juice of ½ lemon
½ tsp smoked paprika
2 tsp finely chopped dill

Mash the chickpeas in a bowl until most are broken up.

Add all the remaining ingredients and mix well. Season to taste.

TIP: *Look out for a good-quality shop-bought mayonnaise to make this recipe, checking the label to ensure that it contains recognisable ingredients (oil, eggs, vinegar, salt) and minimal emulsifiers, additives or preservatives. Organic options are usually good.*

Beetroot and Dill Borani

This jewel-bright, tangy dip is a welcome alternative to hummus. I love it slathered on oat biscuits or spread in a wrap with some toasted seeds and salad leaves, alongside a bowl of soup. It's such a beautiful colour.

VEGETARIAN / GF
Serves 4
Prep time: 10 mins

2 medium cooked and peeled beetroot (about 170g)
30g feta
30g (about 1 tbsp) thick plain yoghurt
1 tbsp fresh lemon juice
10g walnuts, roughly chopped
1 tbsp chopped fresh dill

Place the beetroot, feta and a splash of water in a blender and blitz to make a think, smooth purée. You might need to scrape down the edges a couple of times as you do so.

Stir in the yoghurt and lemon juice and season with salt and pepper.

Serve with the walnuts and dill scattered over the top.

Green Hummus

Hummus has become one of those staples that is pretty much always on hand in my fridge to make a quick sandwich or snack. If time is short, then there is nothing wrong with shop-bought, but homemade is far cheaper, speedy to make and doesn't use so much single-use plastic packaging. Perking it up with additional vegetables – spinach leaves in this case – also helps boost the nutrient and fibre content a little.

VEGAN / GF /DF
Serves 6-8
Prep time: 8 mins
Cook time: 45 mins

1 x 400g tin of chickpeas, drained
   and rinsed
3 tbsp tahini
juice of 2 lemons, plus zest of 1
2 cloves garlic
large handful of baby leaf spinach
large handful of fresh herbs of your
   choice (I use coriander, parsley
   and basil)
½ level tsp salt

Place all the ingredients in a blender and blitz to a smooth paste. You may need to add a couple of splashes of water to get the right consistency. Add 1 tablespoon at a time and blitz until it all combines.

Taste and adjust the seasoning.

To serve, chop up some vegetable dippers, or grab a handful of salad and add some bread, olives or seeds and you're ready to go. I also love it as a filling in a baked potato (or even on toast for a savoury breakfast). You could also add extra greens to ready-made hummus, too – just blitz them in along with a squeeze of lemon juice. If you don't have any fresh herbs, you can leave them out, but I find they do help enhance the flavour.

Keeps in the fridge for 3–4 days or the freezer for up to 3-4 months.

TIP: *This recipe makes enough to provide you with a week's worth of lunches. Serve with wraps, vegetable dippers, lettuce cups or on toast.*

Smoky Kidney Bean Dip

For those who don't like hummus, this is for you. A really economical recipe and a great one to reach for when it feels like there's nothing left to eat in the kitchen apart from one tin of kidney beans lurking in the back of the cupboard! Kids usually like it too, perhaps with some toasted tortillas, corn chips, wraps or crispy baked pitta along with a lovely selection of dipping vegetables (such as chopped carrots, cucumber, sugar snap peas, cherry tomatoes etc.).

VEGAN / GF / DF / KIDS
Serves 4 as a dip or 2 as a main
Prep time: 5 mins

1 × 400g tin of red kidney beans, drained and rinsed
1 small clove garlic, crushed
2 tsp smoked paprika
2 tbsp olive oil
juice of ½ lemon

Place all the ingredients in a blender and blitz until smooth, scraping down the sides a couple of times as you do so. You might need to add a few splashes of water to get the right consistency. Add 1 tablespoon at a time and blitz until it all combines (just 1–2 tablespoons is usually enough).

Taste and adjust the seasoning.

Cornbread

This is a lovely sunny bread to enjoy with soups and salads. It can be frozen in slices, which are best defrosted before warming through in a dry frying pan. I serve this with slices of avocado, cooked cherry tomatoes and a lovely green salad or perhaps as a side to my Chickpea, Butternut and Coconut Soup (see page 98).

VEGETARIAN / (GF) / (DF) / KIDS
Makes 1 loaf or 8-10 slices
  Prep time: 10 mins
Cook time: 40-50 mins

1 × 198g tin of sweetcorn, drained
2 spring onions, trimmed and sliced
2 large free-range eggs, whisked
80g plain flour (use plain gluten-free, if necessary)
1 tsp baking powder (use gluten-free, if necessary)
½ tsp bicarbonate of soda
1 tbsp sunflower seeds
1 tsp smoked paprika
165g dried polenta
225ml milk of choice
pinch of salt

For the topping (optional)
50g feta cheese, crumbled
8 slices of green chilli, deseeded

Preheat the oven to 180°C fan/200°C/gas 6 and line a 900g loaf tin with parchment paper.

In a large bowl, mix all of the ingredients together.

Pour the mixture into the loaf tin and sprinkle over the crumbled feta and sliced green chilli, if using. Bake in the oven for 40-50 minutes until cooked.

Allow to cool in the tin for 10 minutes before turning out and slicing.

Store in an airtight container in the fridge (for 3-4 days), or in the freezer for up to 1 month.

Making flavoured butters is a simple thing to do, but is something I often forget about so I am adding these recipes as a reminder to me as well as to you. These last in the fridge for 2 weeks and can also be frozen. I suggest rolling the butter into a log, wrapping it in parchment paper and popping it in the freezer. Then simply slice off a 1cm disc as and when you need it and add it directly to your cooking.

Chilli and Lime Butter

This adds lots of taste without lots of effort. Use on top of steamed veg, baked fish or chicken for a gentle hit of flavour. One of my go-to, quick meals is to add it to steamed tenderstem broccoli and poached chicken to make a very simple supper suddenly seem more exciting.

VEGETARIAN / GF
Prep time: 5 mins

125g salted butter, softened
zest of 1 lime
1 red chilli, finely chopped
pinch of salt and pepper

Mix all the ingredients together and keep in an airtight container in the fridge for 2 weeks, but best to freeze and use within a month – just slice as and when it's needed.

Tarragon Butter

Add this butter to steamed vegetables, bean stews, baked fish or chicken. It is a great hack for making a plain tin of beans more appealing – just drain the beans and gently warm them through, then stir in the flavoured butter and serve immediately.

VEGETARIAN / GF
Prep time: 5 mins

125g salted butter, softened
2 tbsp finely chopped tarragon
zest of 1 lemon
pinch of pepper

Mix all the ingredients together and store in an airtight container in the fridge for 2 weeks, but best to freeze and use within a month – just slice as and when it's needed.

Parsley and Garlic Butter

This is probably one of the simplest recipes, but it makes a wonderful difference when added to steamed vegetables, bean stews, baked fish or chicken. If you don't eat dairy, you can also freeze herbs in olive oil in ice-cube trays for a similar effect.

VEGETARIAN / GF
Prep time: 5 mins

125g salted butter, softened
6 tbsp finely chopped fresh parsley
3 small cloves garlic, crushed

Mix all the ingredients together and wrap in parchment paper or keep in an airtight container in the fridge for 2 weeks, but best to freeze and use within a month – just slice as and when it's needed.

TIP: *Feel free to swap the parsley for coriander or basil instead. It freezes well, so is a good way to use up leftover fresh herbs that you don't want to waste.*

Cavolo Nero and Walnut Pesto

Pesto is traditionally made with basil and pine nuts. But I make all sorts of versions using different nuts and greens, to increase the variety of what I eat and to make the most of seasonal produce throughout the year. Shop-bought pesto works fine, but homemade is quick to make and tastes better. Serve with pasta, spread on toast with a fried egg, drizzle over cooked vegetables or salads, or mash with a can of plain beans to make a great sandwich filling.

(VEGAN) / GF / (DF) / KIDS
Serves 12
Prep time: 10 mins
Cook time: 5 mins

1 head of cavolo nero (about 200g)
1 clove garlic
60g pecorino or Parmesan (or vegan alternative), grated
50g walnuts, toasted
zest and juice of 1 lemon
60ml extra virgin olive oil, plus some extra, to taste

Strip the cavolo nero leaves from the thick central stem, then wash and roughly chop the leaves. Steam for 4 minutes until wilted.

Place the leaves and all the other ingredients in a blender, along with a couple of splashes of water, and blitz to a pesto that's almost smooth. Taste and season.

Transfer to a jar and loosen with some extra oil to your preferred consistency.

Store in the fridge and use within 5 days.

Gremolata

This traditional Italian condiment often calls for pine nuts, but I find that toasted almonds bring extra richness and crunch (and are that bit more economical than pine nuts), so I often use them instead. But frankly, any nuts will work well. This is a great way to add instant interest to very simple meals. I spoon it over cooked vegetables, grilled meat or a plain salad. It keeps in the fridge for up to 5 days.

VEGAN / GF / DF
Serves 5–6
Prep time: 5–10 mins

50g toasted almonds, roughly
    chopped (I like a variety of textures,
    some fine, some a little coarser)
zest and juice of 1 lemon
2 tbsp extra-virgin olive oil
1 small clove garlic, crushed
handful of finely chopped parsley

Mix all the ingredients together and season to taste.

Tip: *If you're in a rush, skip toasting the almonds and simply pulse all the ingredients together a few times in the food processor until blended (though do still crush the garlic first).*

Miso Marinade

This marinade will elevate the simplest of ingredients and delivers a big burst of flavour. It's a great way to transform a few really simple ingredients into quite a fancy supper, so try it with chicken, fish, aubergine, butternut squash, prawns and tofu.

VEGAN / (GF) / DF
Makes 5 tbsp (85g)
Prep time: 5 mins

2 tbsp sweet white miso paste
1 tbsp tamari (or soy sauce)
1 thumb-size piece of fresh root
   ginger, peeled and grated
1 small clove garlic, crushed
1 tbsp neutral-flavoured cooking oil
   (I use a light olive oil)

Mix all the ingredients together in a bowl.

Pour over whatever it is you wish to marinate and leave covered in the fridge for (ideally) a minimum of 2 hours or overnight.

> **TIP:** *Use this Miso Marinade to make the , Tofu, Mushroom and Broccoli Traybake on page 125.*

Salsa Verde

I make many different variations of this to add flavour to simple meals. Salsa verde translates literally as 'green sauce' from Spanish, and a Mexican version is made with tomatillos and coriander. You can chop and change this recipe, depending on what fresh herbs you have or like and what you're serving it with. Some classic pairings are: a tarragon-heavy dressing for roast chicken, mint is great with lamb, and parsley always works well with white fish or vegetables.

(VEGAN) / GF / DF
Makes 1 small jar
Prep time: 10 mins

2 handfuls of fresh herbs of your
    choice (tarragon, basil, chives,
    parsley, chervil, coriander or mint)
1 tbsp Dijon mustard
5 tbsp extra-virgin olive oil
zest and juice of 1 lemon
1 tbsp white wine vinegar
6 cornichons
1 tsp capers
1 tsp honey or maple syrup (optional)

Place all the ingredients in a blender and blitz to your preferred consistency.

Season to taste with salt and pepper, and adjust the vinegar and sweetness to get the balance you prefer.

TIP: *Making a Salsa Verde can be a great way of using up any spare fresh herbs, rather than letting them go to waste. It can be frozen, too.*

Pickled Chillies

These need to be made a month or so in advance of when you want to eat them but you'll be so grateful to have them in your fridge when a bland meal needs a lift. The heat of the chilli is mellowed with the pickling process, so they give out a lovely warmth, rather than setting mouths on fire. I love them over eggs, on salads, in curries, soups and stews.

VEGAN / GF / DF

Makes 1 jar

Prep time: 10 mins plus sterilising and cooling time

5 large red or green chillies, washed and chopped into 1cm-thick slices

125ml white wine vinegar

40g caster sugar

8 whole peppercorns

1 star anise

1 bay leaf

Sterilise a clean 350ml jar.

Place all the chopped chillies in the jar.

In a small saucepan, mix 125ml water with the vinegar, sugar, peppercorns, star anise and bay leaf and bring to the boil. Allow to rapidly boil for 1 minute, making sure all the sugar has dissolved, then pour the boiling liquid and the spices over the chillies in the jar.

Seal, then allow to cool for about 30 minutes before storing in fridge.

Leave for 1 month before opening and trying them. By this time, the heat should have mellowed somewhat. Use within 1 month once opened.

TIP: *To sterilise jars, wash the jars and lids with hot, soapy water then place onto a clean roasting tray and put into a warm oven (around 150ºC) for 15–20 minutes. Use an oven glove to remove them and leave until they are cool enough to handle. You can also sterilise jars in a microwave if you have one. After washing with hot soapy water, put them in while still wet and turn on high for 30 seconds.*

Romesco Sauce

This is a versatile, classic Spanish sauce that was originally thought to have been created to go with seafood but is now used widely around the world for many dishes. I rarely stick precisely to this recipe, but vary it depending on what I have to hand. It makes a wonderful sauce for any roasted vegetables and is a lovely addition to roasted chicken or baked fish.

(VEGAN) / GF / DF
Prep time: 5 mins
Cook time: 10 mins

50g whole blanched almonds
180g roasted peppers from a jar, drained
1 clove garlic, crushed
1 tsp smoked paprika
1 tsp ground cumin
pinch of chilli flakes (more if you'd like it spicier, or omit)
1 tsp honey (use maple syrup, if vegan)
1 tbsp sherry vinegar
2 tbsp extra-virgin olive oil

Preheat the oven to 160°C fan/180°C/gas 4.

Place the almonds on a small baking tray and roast for 10 minutes.

Place all the remaining ingredients in a blender, add the roasted almonds and season with salt and pepper. Blitz to a thick paste, but try to keep a few chunks (I prefer it not too smooth).

Adjust the seasoning to taste and serve or store (see below).

TIP: *This sauce lasts well in the fridge but you can also freeze it for up to 3 months. You could freeze portions in ice-cube trays and just pop one or two out every time you need a bit of extra zing for your veggies, fish or chicken.*

Almond and Plum Cake

This is an easy dairy- and gluten-free cake recipe, and the plums can be replaced with various other fruits, depending on what's in season. Berries, thinly sliced apples and rhubarb would all work well – in fact, a rule of thumb is if the fruit you want to use can be made into a compote, then you can use it in this cake. It is really light and doesn't use too much sugar, yet it still hits the spot with a cup of tea after lunch.

VEGETARIAN / GF / DF / KIDS
Serves 8
Prep time: 10 mins
Cook time: 50 mins, plus 10 mins
   cooling time

4 large free-range eggs, separated
70g golden caster sugar
180g ground almonds
60ml almond milk
zest of 1 lemon
pinch of salt
¼ tsp baking powder
200g plums, stones removed and cut
   into 1cm slices

Preheat the oven to 160°C fan/180°C/gas 4 and line an 18cm cake tin with parchment paper.

In a large bowl, mix the egg yolks, sugar, ground almonds, almond milk, lemon zest, salt and baking powder together until it is a thick, smooth paste.

In a separate, very clean bowl, whisk the egg whites until stiff peaks form.

Mix a third of the egg white into the almond mixture and stir well. Fold in the remaining two thirds as carefully as possible until the whole mixture is just combined. Don't overmix, as you'll knock the air out of the egg whites and end up with a heavier cake.

Spoon into the prepared tin and scatter over the sliced plums. Bake for 40–50 minutes until browned on top and cooked through. A skewer or knife poked into the cake should come out clean or with just a few crumbs attached.

Allow to cool for 10 minutes before removing from the cake tin and turning out onto a wire rack to cool.

Store in an airtight container for 3-4 days.

Chocolate Courgette Cake with Rich Chocolate Icing

This is a showstopper of a cake and perfect for a celebration. Courgette cake isn't a new idea, but it pairs so well with chocolate, and really helps to stop the cake drying out. Plus, I'm always keen for original ways to use up my summer courgette glut. Either way, this is such a good cake, no one need ever know it's hiding a good serving of vegetables, unless you feel the need to divulge.

VEGETARIAN / (GF) / (DF) /KIDS
Serves 8–10
Prep time: 15 mins
Cook time: 35 mins

100g dark chocolate (with at least 70% cocoa solids, dairy free if necessary)
200g courgette, grated
80ml mild olive oil
2 large free-range eggs
50g plain yoghurt (or coconut yoghurt, if dairy-free)
70g caster sugar
150g self-raising flour (use gluten-free, if necessary)
½ tsp bicarbonate of soda
pinch of salt
30g dark chocolate chips (optional)

For the icing
100g dark chocolate (with at least 70% cocoa solids, dairy free if necessary)
4 tbsp cream cheese (or coconut yoghurt, if dairy-free)
1 tbsp maple syrup or honey
pinch of salt

Preheat the oven to 160°C fan/180°C/gas 4 and line a 18cm round cake tin with parchment paper.

Melt the dark chocolate for the cake in a heatproof bowl over a pan of simmering water (or in a microwave if you have one), making sure the base of the bowl does not touch the water.

In a large bowl, mix the grated courgette, oil, eggs, yoghurt, melted chocolate and sugar.

In a separate bowl, combine the flour, bicarbonate of soda and salt. Stir the flour mixture into the courgette mix until just combined, then stir in the chocolate chips, if using.

Pour into the tin and bake for about 30–35 minutes (until a skewer comes out clean). Allow to cool for 10 minutes before turning out of the tin.

Meanwhile, to make the icing, melt the dark chocolate as before and set aside to cool for 5 minutes. Stir in the cream cheese (or yoghurt), syrup or honey and salt until smooth.

When the cake is completely cool, spread the icing over the top and sides and serve.

TIP: *As this cake contains fresh ingredients, it's best kept in the fridge (use within 3 days). I prefer it when the icing is a little softer, though, so take it out of the fridge 10–15 minutes before serving.*

Dates with Almond and Chocolate

I rarely make dessert and generally try to keep things simple with some fresh fruit and natural yoghurt. But when I am entertaining, there is often a pressure to offer up something sweet at the end of the meal. These stuffed dates require minimal effort but offer maximum taste. They are still high in sugar but they taste decadently rich, so 1 or 2 feels plenty, and the sugar here comes alongside some fibre, essential nutrients and healthy fats.

(VEGAN) / GF / DF / KIDS
Makes 10
Prep time: 20 mins plus freezing

10 Medjool dates
5 heaped tsp almond butter (or other nut butter of choice)
100g dark chocolate (with at least 70% cocoa solids, dairy free if necessary)
large pinch of flaky sea salt

Line a baking tray with parchment paper.

Carefully cut the dates open on one side and remove the seeds.

Put ½ teaspoon of almond butter in each date where the seed was. Gently squeeze them closed and place in the freezer for 1 hour.

Melt the chocolate in a heatproof bowl over a pan of simmering water (or in a microwave if you have one), making sure the bottom of the bowl doesn't touch the water.

Place one date at a time in the melted chocolate and turn it until covered, then lift it out, allow any excess to run off back into the bowl, and place it on the prepared tray. Repeat until all the dates are covered in chocolate.

Sprinkle each one with a little salt and place back in the freezer to set.

Take out of the freezer at least 10 minutes before serving, so they aren't too solid.

TIP: *Omit the flaky salt if serving to children.*

Earl-Grey-infused Walnut, Date and Honey Cake

This cake always brings a smile to my day when I get time to bake it. Sticky and filling, it satisfies a sweet craving without heaps of processed sugar – using a spoonful of honey, dates and orange juice instead. The secret is the syrup, which keeps it wonderfully moist. It's a great one to bring along on walks or picnics as its robust texture means it keeps its shape.

VEGETARIAN / (GF) / KIDS
Makes 6–8 slices
Prep time: 20–25 mins
Cook time: 35 mins

150g unsalted butter, softened
8 pitted dates, finely chopped
pinch of salt
½ tsp vanilla extract
2 tbsp honey (about 40g)
3 large free-range eggs
150g self-raising wholemeal flour
   (use gluten-free, if necessary)
70g walnuts, roughly chopped

For the syrup
1 tbsp honey (about 20g)
2 Earl Grey tea bags
zest and juice of 1 orange

Preheat the oven to 160°C fan/180°C/gas 4 and line an 18cm cake tin with parchment paper.

In a large bowl, beat the softened butter, dates, salt, vanilla and honey until pale and creamy. Add the eggs one by one, beating very well between each egg so the mixture doesn't curdle.

Sift in the flour, add the chopped walnuts and fold together until just combined.

Spoon the batter into the prepared tin, smoothing the top, and bake for 30–35 minutes until the cake is golden and just cooked.

Meanwhile, mix the honey with 100ml water in a small saucepan, add the tea bags and orange zest and bring to the boil. Reduce the heat and simmer until the liquid has reduced by half. Set aside.

When the cake is out of the oven, but still warm and in its tin, use a skewer to pierce holes about 2cm apart all over the top of the cake. Pour the warm syrup over the top and allow to soak in. Leave in the tin to cool.

Store in an airtight container for 3–4 days.

Chocolate Mousse Pots

This supremely simple and versatile vegan pudding can be finished off with any number of toppings. My favourite garnishes are raspberries and lime zest, or sliced banana and toasted hazelnuts with a bit of whipped coconut cream, but take your pick. You could try sliced poached pears, fresh berries, orange zest or any nuts you like – they're all delicious. You honestly won't believe that this is made with tofu – it's so creamy and smooth.

VEGAN / GF / DF
Serves 4
Prep time: 10 mins, plus 1 hour chilling time

100g dark vegan chocolate (with at least 70% cocoa solids)
300g silken tofu
3 tbsp maple syrup
pinch of salt

Melt the chocolate in a heatproof bowl over a pan of simmering water (or in the microwave, stirring regularly), making sure the bottom of the bowl doesn't touch the water.

Using kitchen paper, try to squeeze/press out as much of the moisture from the silken tofu as possible.

Place the melted chocolate, maple syrup, salt and tofu in a blender and blitz until completely silky smooth.

Pour into glasses, choose a topping to garnish and refrigerate until needed (at least 1 hour). Serve chilled.

TIP: *It's very important to use silken tofu to get a smooth texture.*

Oat, Almond and Berry Traybake

Bakewell tarts always transport me to childhood. They're a very nostalgic dessert, and something I craved endlessly when pregnant. To satisfy my love of this classic, I have been working on creating a slightly healthier and simpler version. You can use either fresh or frozen cherries or berries for this recipe. This doesn't have too much sweetness so if you are used to having sweet things, then increase the sweetener to your desired taste.

VEGAN / GF / DF / KIDS
Makes 12 slices
Prep time: 5 mins
Cook time: 15 mins

400g oats
500ml almond milk (or milk
  of choice)
2 eggs (use chia eggs for a
  vegan version)
2 tbsp maple syrup or honey
1 tsp baking powder
1 tsp vanilla extract
1 tsp almond extract (optional)
150g raspberries (fresh or frozen,
  both work)
2 tbsp chia jam (or any low sugar
  jam if you prefer)
1 tbsp flaked almonds (optional)

For the chia jam
Makes one small jar
2 tbsp chia seeds
250g fresh or frozen berries of choice
1 tbsp honey or maple syrup

Heat the oven to 160°C fan/180°C/gas 4.

Put all the ingredients other than the raspberries/ berries, jam and almonds into a large bowl and mix well.

Put the raspberries into a rectangular baking tray (mine is 9 x 13 inches). Then pour over the oat mix. Sprinkle the almond flakes on top and put into the oven for 15 minutes.

Remove from the oven and leave to cool completely.

Spoon over the jam of choice (if using). Spoon into a bowl while warm and serve with yoghurt of choice, or leave to cool and cut into slices.

Store in an airtight container in the fridge for up to 3 days.

Chia Jam

To make the chia jam, add the berries to a pan on a low heat and bring up to a slight simmer. Give the fruit a bit of a mash using the back of a spoon. Then add the chia seeds and stir well. Remove the pan from the heat and leave for about 5 minutes until the chia seeds have bulked up and the jam is looking thick. Put into a clean container.

Lasts for 1 week covered in the fridge or frozen for 3 months.

TIP: *To make one chia egg, mix 1 tbsp of chia seeds with 2.5 tbsp of warm water and stir well. Leave for 5 – 10 minutes to thicken. Use one chia egg per egg in the recipe.*

PART FIVE

Eat

HOW TO EAT

There is so much written about what to eat, it's perhaps unsurprising that we often overlook *how* we eat. Or at least, we don't give it much thought or sense of importance. Yet in my experience, the care we put into serving ourselves and the habits we develop around mealtimes are often really important missing pieces of the healthy eating puzzle.

I have often met clients who have noticed a significant shift in their general sense of wellbeing, weight and even some symptoms, simply by changing the *way* they serve and enjoy their meals. This is without changing a single thing about their diet, cooking or food choices.

I therefore wanted to share with you some of the favourite 'non-food' eating strategies that I and my clients have found most helpful over the years.

As always, please just take what serves (quite literally in some cases) from this section, and leave the rest. I am sharing a range of ideas and strategies here, but we don't need to do it all. Perhaps start with just one idea, maybe using smaller plates sometimes, or putting phones away in a box at mealtimes and see how that feels and works. Then choose another. Remember – one tiny shift that we manage to maintain for the long run is always better than doing everything at once and giving up in a fortnight.

THE SURPRISING INFLUENCE OF PLATES AND GLASSES

Interestingly, the size and colour of our crockery (plates and bowls) and glasses can potentially impact our portion sizes without us noticing. That's because subconsciously, we tend to judge portion size in relation to the size of the plate or bowl we are serving from or to, rather than the actual portion itself.

So, a portion of food placed on a large plate or bowl can *appear* smaller than the same portion placed on a smaller plate or bowl (see illustration opposite).

This isn't a hard-or-fast rule, of course. And it's likely to impact some of us more than others, or to influence us more or less depending on our circumstances and context.

But you could potentially use this knowledge to your advantage in two ways:

1. If you want to reduce your portion sizes and still signal to your mind that you have had a complete and filling meal, you could try using slightly smaller plates or bowls.

2. If you want to stimulate your appetite, or encourage yourself or your loved ones to eat more, you could try serving the food on a larger plate, which helps to make the portion appear more manageable.

TIP: *This only applies to food served from a bowl or a plate, which is a good reason to try to avoid snacking standing up, or eating on the go. Seeing our food served properly is important for our brains to get the visual message that we have eaten it.*

The takeaway from this point is that it can be helpful to have a few different-sized plates and bowls to hand. For example, I have a selection of 25–28cm dinner plates, smaller side plates, large salad bowls (which are actually pasta bowls, but I often use them for salad) and smaller dessert bowls which I also use for breakfasts or soups. I can then choose whichever bowl or plate I think best complements the meal, with both aesthetics and nutrition in mind.

> **TIP:** *Look for rice bowls, if you're after small dessert bowls. They're great for serving a moderate portion of fruit compote and yoghurt, or other sweet desserts. Charity shops and second-hand shops are also brilliant places to look out for smaller-sized crockery without spending a fortune.*

WINE AND WATER GLASSES

This same portion-size illusion may also work for glassware and drinks. It's something I have encouraged many clients to consider if they need or want to reduce their intake of alcohol, or indeed to increase their water consumption.

If you struggle to remember to drink enough water during the day, perhaps try drinking from larger water glasses, and keep a jug or water bottle on the table during meals (or at any other time you'd like to be drinking more water – at your desk, in the garden, by the bed etc.), so there is no barrier to drinking more as and when you need to.

In contrast, wine glasses can be enormous – there has definitely been a trend towards the 'bucket' glass into which we could fit practically a whole bottle of wine. In fact, the size of wine glasses has reportedly increased sevenfold in the past 300 years or so (from around 70ml in 1700 to 250ml in 2017), with a marked increase in size since the 1990s. I'd therefore recommend looking out for the smallest wine glasses you can find instead, ideally around 125ml size.

Generally, we are more satisfied with one whole smaller glass of wine than we are with half a larger glass. In other words, we use the relative fullness of a glass to judge how much we are drinking, rather than the absolute volume of the wine itself.

It's also easier to keep track of how much we are drinking if we know that one small glass of wine (125ml) is about 1.5 units of alcohol. As a comparison, one large glass of wine (250ml) is 3 units of alcohol and more than a fifth of our recommended weekly intake. The NHS recommends that we all drink less than 14 units of alcohol per week, and no more than 2–3 units per day. I generally suggest my clients aim for no more than 10 units a week, consumed alongside a meal, with at least 2–3 alcohol-free days. For many clients, I actually advise stopping drinking altogether, perhaps if they need to optimise sleep, blood sugar control, menopausal health or weight, for example. This has been made a lot simpler now there are so many good, grown-up, non-alcoholic drinks available.

HEALTHY SERVING TIPS AND TRICKS

So, the kitchen is organised, the meal planning done, shopping bought, ingredients prepared and the cooking completed. We've already done such a lot to get to the point of serving up, whether alone or in company. But there are still some tips and tricks that we can use at this point to boost our nutrition and enjoyment of the meal, alongside saving ourselves time and reducing food waste.

1. If we want to ensure that we have enough leftovers (or 'planned-overs') to make into another meal, aim to serve this *first*. Portion however much is needed into a separate container before serving today's meal. This means it's less likely to be inadvertently depleted, leaving us short for tomorrow. It also feels so much more deliberate and considered this way, rather than our future meal being a messy afterthought. This can be particularly important if cooking for one – try to see the leftovers as tomorrow's ready meal and present it like a gift to your future self.

2. Start serving by filling half the plate with vegetables or salad, before adding quarter of a plate of protein (see page 45 for more on this). This guideline also applies if we go back for seconds: still make half of the second portion vegetables. For this reason, I tend to put the vegetable dishes out first, so these are what go onto the plate first.

HEALTHY-EATING TIP: *Try starting your meal by eating the vegetables and protein first (before the carbohydrates). This can be a helpful strategy for balancing blood sugars – and therefore mood, energy and appetite later in the day. I often recommend my clients begin their meal with two bites of protein.*

3. If you are trying to keep a mindful eye on portion sizes, or struggle a little with mindless eating (or eating beyond the point of feeling comfortably full), there are a couple of serving strategies that could help:

•   **Place a cover or lid over the serving dish once you have served yourself.** This not only helps to keep the food warm, but may also reduce the likelihood that you go back quickly for second helpings or eat more than you need. I find that a cover or lid reduces some of the visual stimulus that can be a prompt to eat more. If it's a cold dish, it could be put straight into the fridge before sitting down to eat.

- **Try serving from the counter or kitchen worktops,** rather than bringing the dishes to the table. The simple barrier of having to stand up and walk back for seconds tends to encourage us to think twice before reaching for more. Of course, if you are *really* still hungry, you can get up for another helping, but I find that a moment of mindfulness before reaching out automatically, just because it's in front of us, can be helpful.

- **Keep alcoholic or soft drinks on the side** (or in the fridge and out of sight), rather than on the table during meals. We may be less inclined to go to the effort of standing up and heading over to the fridge to pour another glass, than if it were right in front of us. Keep a jug of cold water close to hand instead.

4. It's best not to keep salt on the table. Most of us would benefit from having less salt in our diet. Having a salt shaker, grinder or cellar on the table acts as a visual cue to add salt to our food, even before tasting it and seeing if it really needs extra seasoning. Try a pepper grinder instead.

HEALTHY EATING TIP: *If you find food bland without adding extra salt at the table, think about adding acidity instead – I find vinegar or lemon / lime juice often reduces the craving for salt.*

WE EAT WITH OUR EYES

The saying goes that we eat with our eyes, and I think this is often true. We instinctively feel that beautiful food is more tempting, and so the way something is served can make a big difference to how much we want to eat it. Advertisers and food stylists use this to their advantage, but home cooks can do the same (albeit on a slightly more casual level).

I think that taking a few seconds to make a healthy plate of food look that little bit more delicious can really help us to enjoy and appreciate our meal more consciously. And perhaps encourage the more reticent to try things that might be outside of their usual comfort zone.

Having said all of that, I am conscious that we don't *need* to line up the blueberries on our morning porridge or arrange our salads into rainbows for them to be healthy, filling and delicious. But when time and inclination allow, it can be a fun, creative outlet at the very least.

How about trying a few of these ideas:

1. **Think about colour.** Eating a wide range of colourful plants is good for our nutrition (as the different colours can provide us with a range of antioxidants and phytonutrients), and it also looks pretty. I try to have at least three colours on the plate – definitely some green – but more is even better.

2. **Add some height.** I'm still not sure why this is, but a plate of food with an element of height seems to look better than one that is flat. So, pile up those vegetables, add a heap of herbs, spoon sauces onto meat or fish, and don't be afraid of centring elements on the plate atop each other.

3. **Edible flowers** are simple and striking decorations to add to salads, desserts or cakes. A few go a long way and some have distinctive and delicious flavours.

4. **Leave a little space.** While I am all for filling a plate with nourishing food, leaving a little white space around the food can make it look a bit more refined.

5. **Think beyond the food.** Taking a moment to clear and lay the table, adjust the lighting, turn down the music or take off your apron before dinner can all help set the scene.

'Not everyone in Italy may know how to cook, but nearly everyone knows how to eat. Eating in Italy is one more manifestation of the Italian's age-old gift of making art out of life'
Marcella Hazan

THE JOY OF MINDFUL EATING

We've covered organising, planning, shopping and cooking and have finally made it to the eating part of the book!

The act of eating is usually so ingrained and automatic (and influenced by so many external factors, from work, stress and family life to fatigue), we don't always see or notice its potential significance.

Yet if my years of experience have taught me anything, eating well quite literally requires us to eat well. And, to me, that really means eating mindfully, truly tasting and savouring each mouthful. However, I think the phrase can sometimes be a little confusing or off-putting. Clients often react very quickly when I raise the topic, saying they don't have time to meditate at mealtimes! Of course, very few of us do, but this comes from a bit of a misunderstanding.

Mindful eating is simply the enjoyment of food with all our senses, and without judgement. It is not necessarily about meditation (although some people may include this in their practice, and combining mealtimes with a meditative or mindful practice could be a great idea if time is short and stress is high).

Instead, I generally interpret mindful eating to mean:

1. Briefly noticing, without judging ourselves, how our body feels before eating. *For example: Are we very hungry? Not so hungry? A bit thirsty? Tired? Excited? Distracted? Stressed? Anxious?*

2. Being aware of the fact we are eating, rather than being mostly distracted by work, reading, the TV, social media, radio, podcasts, music or similar.

3. Observing the sight, smell and taste of the food as we eat it. Paying attention!

4. Noting how our body feels after eating, again, without judgement. *For example*: *Do we feel comfortably satisfied? Energised? Full? Sluggish? A bit bloated? This helps us to tune into the physical feedback that our body shares with our minds after a meal.*

These four steps take very little time and, with practice and consistency, can rapidly become our 'new normal'. However, it's natural for our mind to wander and for all sorts of other thoughts to creep in while we are eating. The practice is much more about setting the intention to pay attention, rather than forcing 100% concentration.

Ultimately, the point of mindful eating is to savour the pleasures of good food, and to start to listen to what our body is saying to us when we eat. This is important, not least because good food is one of the greatest pleasures in life, but also because our body cannot use words. It can only use signs, symptoms and feelings to communicate with our brains.

To pick up on these (often subtle) cues, we need to listen. Sometimes they are only whispers. And listening to our bodies, like learning any sort of language, does require a bit of practice and attention. Especially if we're out of the habit and have been eating on auto-pilot for years. Mindful eating is one of the best ways to help develop this habit of listening and attentively responding to what our bodies need.

To help get us started, here are eight everyday strategies that we can use to help remind us to eat more mindfully:

1. **Make time to eat** We have to eat. To overlook this essential human requirement, and to think that everything else is more important than taking time to nourish our bodies is a little strange, if you think about it! So, where possible, start to schedule in mealtimes. Even if it is just 15 minutes three times a day, it adds up to less than 5% of our waking hours. I think we all deserve that at the very least. When working with clients, one of the first things I'll do is help them to schedule in their meals between meetings, encouraging them to think about changing their schedule to allow time to eat. It sounds crazy, doesn't it? But so many of us forget to eat, relying on snacks or making do without instead. So, give yourself the grace of three meals a day, and the time to actually eat them.

2. **Set the table** A laid table, perhaps with a candle in the evening, is a visual cue that encourages and reminds us to slow down and savour our food a little more. It takes just a few seconds but can make a world of difference. It can be as simple as putting the cutlery and a glass on the table, or as elaborate as creating a beautiful tablescape complete with linens, flowers and decorations. The choice is yours, but setting the scene for a relaxed meal certainly seems to help us to slow down.

3. **Sit down to eat, ideally at a table** Challenge yourself to never eat standing, if sitting at a table is an option. This includes eating snacks. It's amazing how much more satisfying and filling a snack feels if we decant it from the packaging and eat it off a plate (or bowl), while sitting at a table. Even better if we then eat it undistracted too.

4. **Breathe first** Take 1–3 long, slow, deep breaths once you're sitting down, but before you start eating. Breathing is one of the quickest and easiest ways of reminding our nervous system to enter the 'rest and digest' mode (and to switch off from 'fight, flight or freeze'). This is the optimal state for our bodies to be in when eating, helping to maximise the goodness we can digest and absorb from our food. It helps tell our digestive organs to do their job, sending more blood to our gastrointestinal tract to absorb the incoming nutrients.

5. **Try to avoid screens while eating** Keep an opaque box (out of sight of the table) that is specifically for putting phones, laptops and tablets in at mealtimes. Perhaps even switch them to airplane or silent mode, if possible. Use this box at every mealtime, no exceptions, for two weeks and see how you get on. I'm going to hazard a guess that it's a habit you'll want to keep long after the fortnight is up. This strategy also helps to hold adults to the same standards as we often request from children and teens. Don't forget to turn off the TV, if there is one visible from your table, too. Remember, it's OK *not* to multi-task while you are eating.

6. **Swap hands** Try swapping your knife and fork around, so you're eating and chopping with your non-dominant hand. It feels uncomfortable and strange so our brains are constantly reminded that this is a mindfulness practice and keeps us coming

back to the senses. It also really helps to slow down eating. Another tactic to help slow us down, if we tend to race through meals, is to put your fork down between bites and to finish chewing that mouthful before picking the fork back up for the next. It's simple, but effective.

7. **Chew, chew and then chew some more** Slowing down meals and eating without distraction certainly helps us to chew more, but I often see people wolf their food down with barely a single chew. Remember, our stomachs don't have teeth. Chewing is the primary stage of digestion and is vital for helping our gut to extract the optimal amount of nutrients from our food. As a very basic rule of thumb, inadequate chewing = inadequate digestion.

8. **Talk about the food** If you are dining with your partner, family or others, don't be afraid to talk about the food. The only caveat to this is to try to avoid discussing the food in a judgemental manner (especially how healthy – or not – you think it is) or commenting on how much (or little) you or they have eaten. Instead, discuss how the food looks, smells and tastes. Talk about how it was cooked, how it was produced, and ponder the myriad people in the supply chain who helped to bring it to your table. Reminisce about previous meals that you have enjoyed, how your dining companions are finding it, and what you'd like to try in the future. Celebrate the privilege and joy of the food in front of you, as it is indeed a privilege to have choices about what and how to eat in a world where so many don't.

'Don't chew your worries, your fear, or your anger. If you chew your planning and your anxiety, it's difficult to feel grateful for each piece of food. Just chew your food.'
Thich Nhat Hanh

Sometimes, especially when we start out with mindful eating, we can meet quite a bit of mental resistance. Perhaps we're really used to eating with lots of distractions, so sitting and eating without screens or in silence can feel a bit boring, uncomfortable or lonely. Or perhaps we notice negative or judgemental thoughts come racing into our minds. But try to stick with it. Even if just for a couple of moments at the start of the meal, and notice if those feelings start to subside over time. Everyone has a different experience of mindful eating, so I just wanted to say that you are not alone if it's not effortless to begin with. It wasn't for me, but it has got easier (and more enjoyable) with practice. If, however, it doesn't start to feel easier, or the thoughts or emotions you're feeling around food are quite overwhelming, then reach out for professional support. Food can be a deeply emotional topic, and it is never a sign of weakness to ask for help.

IN SUMMARY

1. Eating well requires us to, quite literally, eat well.

2. Choose crockery or glasses with both nutrition and aesthetics in mind. A portion of food on a large plate can potentially *appear* smaller than if that same portion of food was on a smaller plate.

3. Use the smallest wine glasses you can find. On the whole, a smaller glass of wine feels more satisfying than half a bigger glass (even though the volume is the same). Ideally stick to less than 10 units of alcohol per week (if indeed you drink at all).

4. Serve your 'planned overs' beautifully and first.

5. Keep salt, wine, soft drinks and serving platters off the table, if you'd like to be more mindful about how much of these things you consume in a meal.

6. Have a play with making food beautiful. We eat with our eyes and so making healthy food look as appetising as possible can be a helpful tactic to get us eating outside of our comfort zone.

7. Don't underestimate the nutritional transformation and culinary joy that can come through a little mindful eating. If we've bothered to plan, shop, prep and cook the food, it's worth bothering to take the time to sit, taste, enjoy and savour it, too.

AFTERWORD

Thank you for reading this book. If you have followed my advice, I hope you feel a huge sense of achievement, both now and for the years ahead. I truly hope that it has helped you, in one way or another, to feel calmer in the kitchen and take that little step closer to making healthy eating a stress-free way of life. I also hope you have found the organisation cathartic and the advice practical and useful. Above all, I hope it makes your life a bit better.

If you have enjoyed it, I'd be so grateful if you could help spread the word by sharing on socials – I'd love to see your newly organised kitchens, your meal plans, and what recipes you cook. If you use #theorganisedcook I'll be keeping an eye out, but you can also tag me to let me know on Instagram @ameliafreer or Facebook @ameliafreernutrition. I'll be creating lots of specific boards for this book, along with continuing to share recipes on Pinterest @AmeliaFreer.

Thank you again for joining me through this process.

Amelia x

SUSTAINABLE KITCHEN SWAPS

Single use plastic bags (especially for fresh produce)

Reusable cloth bags or no bags (just load unwrapped produce into your big shopping bag at checkout – this saves time when unpacking anyway)

Paper kitchen towels

Sponges, tea-towels, small flannels or e-cloths

Disposable / paper napkins

Washable cloth napkins

Disposable coffee cups

Refillable coffee / 'to-go' cups

Bottled water / soft drinks

Water filter and reusable water bottles (opt for ones with large necks so you can add fresh fruit for flavouring, if liked)

Disposable straws

Metal or silicone reusable straws

Disposable coffee pods

Recyclable coffee pods (or use a cafetière / stove-top coffee pot)

Clingfilm

Beeswax wraps / reusable clip-top storage containers / silicone bowl covers

Aluminium foil

If a recipe calls for a foil cover, try using a large casserole and lid instead. For lining trays, use compostable parchment paper. For storing food, use beeswax wraps or reusable containers.

Plastic storage / sandwich bags

Rinse and reuse those you already have multiple times, and choose reusable silicone bags, or beeswax wraps instead when buying.

Spices in individual containers	Bulk buy spices and decant into old jam jars – this is usually more cost effective too.
Plastic bottles of oil / vinegar	Refillable glass bottles (various delis and zero-waste shops now offer very good olive oil refills, which are often cheaper than buying in bottles, for better-quality oil). Choose tinted rather than clear glass to help preserve the oil.
Plastic-packaged dried goods	Take reusable containers to zero-waste stores, or buy in bulk and decant to reduce packaging overall.
Plastic washing-up gloves	Compostable rubber gloves
Individual plastic bottles of washing up liquid	Buy one reusable bottle and bulk-buy washing liquid / refillable pouches / visit a zero-waste store where they have a refill station.
Plastic single lighter	Wooden matches
Individual plastic bottles of hand soap (or shampoo/conditioner/shower gel etc).	Refillable glass containers (these look lovelier anyway) and take them to be re-filled or buy refill pouches.
Plastic kitchen equipment (utensils, washing up brushes etc.)	Opt for wooden / metal instead, if possible, so they can be recycled or biodegrade at the end of their useable life.

WEEKLY MEAL PLAN

	DAY 1	DAY 2	DAY 3	DAY 4	DAY 5	DAY 6	DAY 7
Breakfast	Seedy Cinnamon Bircher (make enough of the base mix for three servings).	Seasonal Frittata (make double portion to have enough leftovers for lunch tomorrow).	Seedy Cinnamon Bircher as porridge	Breakfast Muffins	Seedy Cinnamon Bircher as muesli	Breakfast Muffins	Leftover Baked Caponata with 1-2 poached eggs. Add a slice of toast if you'd like.
Vegan alternative	*Seedy Cinnamon Bircher Make enough base mix for four portions. Use a plant-based milk / yoghurt.*	*Lemon and Poppy Seed Granola served with plant milk (make enough for at least three portions). 1 serving seasonal fresh fruit.*	*Seedy Cinnamon Bircher as porridge. Use plant milk to make the porridge.*	*Lemon and Poppy Seed Granola served with plant milk. 1 serving seasonal fresh fruit.*	*Seedy Cinnamon Bircher as muesli. Use plant milk over the base for your muesli.*	*Seedy Cinnamon Bircher any way you want it.*	*Lemon and Poppy Seed Granola served with plant milk. 1 serving seasonal fresh fruit.*
Very busy week	Seedy Cinnamon Bircher (make enough for the whole week and vary how you serve it daily)	Seedy Cinnamon Bircher	Seedy Cinnamon Bircher	Seedy Cinnamon Bircher	Seedy Cinnamon Bircher	Seedy Cinnamon Bircher	Seedy Cinnamon Bircher
Lunch	Chickpea, Butternut and Coconut Soup Add a slice of toast if hungry. 1 serving seasonal fresh fruit for dessert.	Green Hummus on rye or GF toast, with a big seasonal side salad of your choice. 1 serving seasonal fresh fruit for dessert.	Leftover Seasonal Frittata Serve with a seasonal side salad of your choice. 1 serving seasonal fresh fruit for dessert.	Leftover Green Hummus with vegetable dippers. If you've got time, make some Seedy Crackers to go with it. 1 serving seasonal fresh fruit for dessert.	Instant Roasted Pepper and Lentil Soup 1 serving seasonal fresh fruit for dessert.	Chickpea Mayo served in lettuce cups with tomatoes and cucumber (or other vegetables of your choice). 1 serving seasonal fresh fruit for dessert.	Kimchi and Feta Salad (or **Kale, Potato and Pecorino Soup** if the weather is colder). Add a slice of toast if you're hungry. 1 serving seasonal fresh fruit for dessert.
Vegan alternative	*N/A*	*N/A*	*Baked Falafel with seasonal salad of your choice and Tahini Dressing.*	*N/A*	*N/A*	*Chickpea Mayo Use a vegan mayonnaise, or opt for the Smoky Kidney Bean Dip.*	*Leftover Baked Caponata on toast with Tahini Dressing and sliced avocado.*
Very busy week	Chickpea, Butternut and Coconut Soup (Make two portions). Add a slice of toast if hungry. 1 serving seasonal fresh fruit for dessert.	Leftover Chickpea, Butternut and Coconut Soup Add a slice of toast if hungry. 1 serving seasonal fresh fruit for dessert.	Green Hummus wraps with salad leaves, tomatoes, red peppers and cucumber. 1 serving seasonal fresh fruit for dessert.	Green Hummus with vegetable dippers Add a slice of toast if hungry. 1 serving seasonal fresh fruit for dessert.	Instant Roasted Pepper and Lentil Soup (Make two portions). 1 serving seasonal fresh fruit for dessert.	Chickpea Mayo with lettuce cups and leftover vegetables. 1 serving seasonal fresh fruit for dessert.	Chickpea Mayo wraps with side salad. 1 serving seasonal fresh fruit for dessert.

	DAY 1	DAY 2	DAY 3	DAY 4	DAY 5	DAY 6	DAY 7
Dinner	**Courgette, Lemon and Mozzarella Pasta** Serve with extra steamed greens or salad of your choice. 1 serving seasonal fresh fruit for dessert.	**Turkey Burgers** served with tomatoes, lettuce, cucumber or steamed greens. Add some steamed new potatoes or a wholemeal pitta if you're hungry. 1 serving seasonal fresh fruit for dessert.	**Quick Fish Pie** served with peas and any other seasonal vegetables of your choice. 1 serving seasonal fresh fruit for dessert.	**One-pot Roasted Lemongrass Chicken** with rice, served with steamed vegetables of your choice. 1 serving seasonal fresh fruit for dessert.	**Pork and Fennel Meatballs in Tomato Sauce** and some steamed vegetables of your choice. Add a moderate portion of wholemeal, spelt or legume pasta if you're hungry. 1 serving seasonal fresh fruit for dessert.	**Baked Caponata** (make a double portion so you have leftovers for breakfast tomorrow) served with grilled halloumi, baked fish or chicken and a side salad if you'd like. 1 serving seasonal fresh fruit for dessert.	**One-pot Green Dahl** with steamed broccoli and green beans. 1-2 **Dates with Almond and Chocolate** for dessert, or opt for a piece of fresh fruit.
Vegan alternative	*Courgette, Lemon and Mozzarella Pasta Omit the mozzarella and add some extra pine nuts. Opt for a legume-based pasta to boost protein intake.*	*Try the Baked Falafel instead of the burgers (make enough for two portions).*	*One-pot Lemon and Cabbage Spaghetti Add a side of tomatoes if you like. Use vegetable stock and vegan cheese. Use a legume-based pasta if possible to boost protein. 1 serving seasonal fresh fruit for dessert.*	*Freekah with Crispy Roast Mushrooms (make enough for two portions). Add a side of steamed greens if you like. 1 serving seasonal fresh fruit for dessert.*	*Leftover Freekah with Crispy Roast Mushrooms. Add a side of seasonal vegetables or roasted tomatoes if you like. 1 serving seasonal fresh fruit for dessert.*	*Baked Caponata served with ½ tin drained and rinsed butter beans per person (make a double portion of caponata). 1 serving seasonal fresh fruit for dessert.*	*One Pot Green Dahl Use dairy-free yoghurt to serve, if you'd like. 1-2 Dates with Almond and Chocolate for dessert, or opt for a piece of fresh fruit.*
Very busy week	**One-pot Green Dahl** with steamed broccoli and green beans (make enough for at least two portions). 1 serving seasonal fresh fruit for dessert.	**Leftover One-pot Green Dahl** with steamed broccoli and green beans. 1 serving seasonal fresh fruit for dessert.	**One-pot Lemon and Cabbage Spaghetti** with a side of tomatoes. Use a legume-based pasta if possible to boost protein. 1 serving seasonal fresh fruit for dessert.	**Quick Fish Curry** with seasonal steamed vegetables (prepare enough curry and vegetables for two servings). Add some rice if hungry. 1 serving seasonal fresh fruit for dessert.	**Leftover Quick Fish Curry** with vegetables 1 serving seasonal fresh fruit for dessert.	**Leftover Instant Roasted Pepper and Lentil Soup.** Add a slice of toast if hungry. 1 serving seasonal fresh fruit for dessert.	**Salmon and Soba Noodles with Peanuts** Add some steamed greens or green beans if you'd like. 1 serving seasonal fresh fruit for dessert.

ENDNOTES

Page 28: **The fridge is not supposed to be a place where food goes to be forgotten. According to the Love Food Hate Waste Campaign**… Chill The Fridge Out. *Love Food Hate Waste*. Accessed August 2022. https://www.lovefoodhatewaste.com/article/chill-fridge-out

Page 46: **…as the vast bulk of food advertising is for ultra-processed foods and drinks that are generally high in fats, sugars and salt.** Folkvord F, Hermans RCJ. Food Marketing in an Obesogenic Environment: a Narrative Overview of the Potential of Healthy Food Promotion to Children and Adults. *Current Addiction Reports*. 2020, 7, 431–436. doi: 10.1007/s40429-020-00338-4.

Page 56: **Some research suggests that we buy fewer fruits and vegetables when shopping online, as we are concerned that they might arrive bruised, overripe or damaged**: Jilcott Pitts S, Ng S, Blitstein J, Gustafson A, Niculescu M. Online grocery shopping: Promise and pitfalls for healthier food and beverage purchases. *Public Health Nutrition*. 2018, 21(18), 3360-3376. doi:10.1017/S1368980018002409

Page 56: **We are reportedly more likely to check out the nutrition information labels when shopping in-person than we are to click into these facts online.** Olzenak K, French S, Sherwood N, Redden JP, Harnack L. How Online Grocery Stores Support Consumer Nutrition Information Needs. *Journal of Nutrition Education and Behaviour*. 2020 Oct, 52(10), 952-957. doi: 10.1016/j.jneb.2020.07.009.

Page 59: **a growing body of evidence suggests that ultra-processed foods are potentially harmful to health, especially when eaten regularly and in large quantities.** Pagliai G, Dinu M, Madarena MP, Bonaccio M, Iacoviello L, Sofi F. Consumption of ultra-processed foods and health status: a systematic review and meta-analysis. *British Journal of Nutrition*. 2021 Feb 14, 125(3), 308-318. doi: 10.1017/S0007114520002688.

Page 59: **research has also suggested that decreasing the amount of ultra-processed foods we eat may substantially improve how nutritious our diet is…**Rauber F, da Costa Louzada ML, Steele EM, Millett C, Monteiro CA, Levy RB. Ultra-Processed Food Consumption and Chronic Non-Communicable Diseases-Related Dietary Nutrient Profile in the UK (2008–2014). *Nutrients*. 2018 May 9, 10(5), 587. doi: 10.3390/nu10050587.

Page 60: **Here are a few things to look out for on labels, which indicate that a food may be ultra-processed:** Monteiro CA, Cannon G, Levy RB, Moubarac JC, Louzada ML et al. Ultra-processed foods: what they are and how to identify them. *Public Health Nutrition*. 2019 Apr, 22(5), 936-941. doi: 10.1017/S1368980018003762.

Page 216: **In fact, the size of wine glasses has reportedly increased sevenfold in the past 300 years or so…** Zupan Z, Evans A, Zupan Z, Evans A, Couturier DL, Marteau TM. Wine glass size in England from 1700 to 2017: a measure of our time. *British Medical Journal*. 2017 Dec 13, 359:j5623. doi: 10.1136/bmj.j5623.

Page 216: **… we use the relative fullness of a glass to judge how much we are drinking, rather than the absolute volume of the wine itself.** Pechey R, Attwood AS, Couturier DL, Munafò MR, Scott-Samuel NE, Woods A, Marteau TM. Does Glass Size and Shape Influence Judgements of the Volume of Wine? *PLoS One*. 2015 Dec 23, 10(12), e0144536. doi: 10.1371/journal.pone.0144536.

Page 216: **The NHS recommends that we all drink less than 14 units of alcohol per week.** National Health Service. Live Well: Alcohol Units. (2021). Accessed August 2022. https://www.nhs.uk/live-well/alcohol-advice/calculating-alcohol-units/

INDEX

burgers 16, *130*, 131, *166*, 167
butter 126, 190, 191, 207
    flavoured *188-9*, 190-1
butter beans 23, 126, 161
butternut squash 91, 98, 194

C
cabbage 65, 116, 126, 147
cakes 200-3, *206*, 207
calories 62
cannellini beans 23, 132, 161
capers 108, 195
Caponata 108, *109*
carrots 31, *63*, 65, 69, 71, 75, 88, 107, 132, 158, 177, 184
caster sugar 196, 200, 203
cauliflower *63*, 71, 75, 122
Cauliflower with Crispy Leaves, Green Lentils and Hazelnut Salsa 122, *123*
cavolo nero 104, 136, 142, 192
Cavolo Nero and Walnut Pesto 192, *192*
celery *63*, 108, 110, 132, 151, 158, 161, 168, 177
chard *63*, 94, 136
cheddar cheese 94, 126, 132, 153
cheeses, *see by type*
Cheesy Baked Beans 132, *133*
cherries *63*, 210
chervil 195
chia eggs 210
Chia Jam 210, *211*
chia seeds 83, 86, 210
chicken 17, 41, 44, 75, 100, 161, 162, 164, 190, 191, 194, 195, 198, 228
Chicken, Courgette and White Bean Stew *160*, 161
Chicken, Leek and Mushroom Pie 162, *163*
Chicken Soup 100, *101*
chicken stock 75, 100, 107, 147, 151, 158, 161, 162, 164, 168, 177
Chickpea, Butternut and Coconut Soup 91, 98, *99*, 187, 228
chickpea flour 140
Chickpea Mayo 180, *181*, 228
chickpeas 23, 41, 42, 98, 110, 128, 180, 182
Chilli and Lime Butter *189*, 190

chilli flakes 45, 95, 98, 104, 107, 140, 144, 157, 173, 198
chillies *63*, 75, 90, 100, 125, 128, 136, 164, 171, 173, 187, 190, 196
chives 158, 195
chocolate 22, 23, 44, 46, 61, 203, 205, 208, 228
Chocolate Courgette Cake with Rich Chocolate Icing *202*, 203
Chocolate Mousse Pots 208, *209*
cinnamon 75, 83, 86, 177, 228
citrus fruits, *see by type*
cleaning 17, 20, 29, 76
    checklists 77-9
    tips/tricks 36, 76-9
clingfilm 226
clutter-free surfaces 18, 21
coconut cream 151, 208
coconut milk 23, 98, 136, 154, 164, 174
coconut oil 23, 85, 126, 136, 154
coconut sugar 88
coconut yoghurt 203
cod 153, 154
coleslaw 16, 69
colour-coding guide 57-9, 60, 61
colourful fruit and veg, importance of 52, 91, 218
composting 20, 70, 77, *226*, 227
compotes 74-5, 83, 200, 216
container labelling/storage 20, 27
cookbooks, advice regarding 21
cooking equipment 12-17
cooking stocks, *see by type*
cooking tips 69-70
cooking utensils 19
coriander 96, 98, 100, 110, 113, 116, 128, 136, 154, 157, 164, 171, 174, 182, 195
Cornbread *186*, 187
cornichons 195
countertop(s) 20-1, 218
Courgette, Lemon and Almond Salad 114, *115*
Courgette, Lemon and Mozzarella Pasta 142, *143*, 228
courgettes *63*, 75, 88, 90, 108, 114, 120, 139, 142, 149, 153, 161, 203
crackers 178, *179*, 180, 228
cream 38, 126

ACKNOWLEDGEMENTS

With thanks…

Creating a book of this sort is a process of many different layers, which is something I never understood before I began writing my own. It starts off as a solitary experience, then over time, more and more people contribute their expertise, and it becomes a collective body of work. I have once again been lucky to work with a team of brilliant people who have all helped this book evolve into something far bigger than my dreams.

My thank yous begin with Rozzie Yoxall for writing this book alongside me. We first brainstormed the idea during lockdown and after many months, lots of juggling motherhood, endless edits, and quite a few tears, we got there. This book wouldn't have been possible without you Rozzie, so thank you, as ever, for all that you do to help me keep afloat. Together, we help lots of people – our incentive from the very start.

Others who contributed were my wonderful friend, the most excellent chef, Katie Randell, who worked on all the recipes. Thank you, Katie, for providing endless food inspiration and always helping me to fall back in love with food when I get overwhelmed. Thank you to Sylvie Odile Saunders for a brainstorm here and there and your clever way with words. Thanks to my PA Mary Goodman for your endless calm and support, both for the book and the rest of my work.

Huge thanks to my publishers Lagom, and Michelle Signore for taking me on, believing in my work and being a brilliant editor, along with your fantastic team: Sophie Nevrkla – a highly efficient editorial assistant; Jo Roberts-Miller – the most brilliant copy editor; Emily Rough – thank you for such a beautiful front cover design; Graeme Andrew – thank you for a gorgeous interior pages design. Thanks also go to Francesca Eades – marketing and social media; Eleanor Stammeijer and Izzy Smith – publicity. Thanks also to all the recipe testers.

My wonderful management team – Bev James, Morwenna Loughmann, Tom Wright and Aoife Rice Murphy – thank you for always championing me with such gusto and encouraging me to take the leap and do this book. You are simply the best team!

Clare Winfield – what a complete joy you are to work with. Thanks for being the calmest presence, for taking the prettiest pictures and even getting me to relax and enjoy being in front of the camera. Thanks to Emma La Haye for your generosity, exquisite styling and props, kindness, and enthusiasm. And to Troy Willis for so casually recreating all my recipes and making them look so pretty.

Philippe Tholimet – this was our 5th book together. You are the only person who can make my hair look good, and thank you for always being there, standing behind the photographer, making me laugh. Sjaniel Turrell, thank you once again for the most natural make up and making me feel confident – you are always the easiest person to be around. Nicola Fleming, thank you for managing all my insecurities by styling and accessorising me, for the shoot as well as in my daily life. Polly Crawley, thank you for brilliantly capturing, editing, and managing my social media, for this book as well as the rest of the time. You were the dream team to do the shoot with and thank you also for being so sensitive and letting me change dates when I needed to.

My loyal readers and supporters of my monthly newsletter and social media, without whom I wouldn't get the opportunity to write books and help a wider amount of people than my one-to-one work allows.

Finally, thank you to my friends and family for their ongoing support for my work and their understanding when I get overwhelmed, stressed, or go quiet. And thank you to my daughter Willow, who missed out on quite a few times with me over the last year while I was locked away in front of my computer and failed to strike the infamous work-life balance. I hope that one day she will be able to enjoy this book and find it helpful too.